Calculated to Please 2

Calculator activities for the National Curriculum

MOUNT PRIMARY SCHOOL
LANE
BEESTON
LEEDS 11

Paul Harling

UNWIN HYMAN

SKILLS AND RESOURCES SERIES

"CALCULATOR METHODS

The attainment targets and programmes of study in mathematics demonstrate a recognition that calculators provide a powerful and versatile tool for pupils to use in both the development of their understanding of number and for doing calculations. Calculators are now an established item of classroom equipment, and should be available for pupils to use at all four key stages.

They provide a fast and efficient means of calculation, liberating pupils and teachers from excessive concentration on pencil and paper methods. By increasing the options available to pupils, by enabling more ambitious exploration of numbers to be undertaken, and by saving time in making calculations, calculators offer an opportunity to increase standards of attainment.

In learning to use calculators, pupils should have the opportunity to:
- become familiar with the number operations to be performed by calculators as they progress through the levels of Attainment Targets 2 and 3;
- explore the way a calculator works through a variety of number games and similar activities;
- develop confidence in selecting correct key sequences for various calculations;
- use mental methods to estimate for expected answers, check for reasonableness and interpret results;
- use calculators as a powerful means of exploring numbers and to extend their understanding of the nature of numbers and number relationships."

National Curriculum Non-Statutory Guidelines: Mathematics (paras 4·0–4·3)

Thanks to Texas Instruments for supplying calculators for the front cover.

Published in 1989 by
UNWIN HYMAN LIMITED
15/17 Broadwick Street
London W1V 1FP

© Paul Harling 1989

The purchase of this copyright material confers the right on the purchasing institution to photocopy the pupils' pages without any specific authorisation by the publisher. No other part of this publication may be reproduced, stored in a retrieval system, or transmitted in any form or by any means, electronic, mechanical, photocopying, recording or otherwise, without the prior permission of Unwin Hyman Limited.

British Library Cataloguing in Publication Data

Harling, Paul
Calculated to please
1. Schools. Curriculum subjects
Mathematics, Teaching aids Electronic calculators
I. Title
510'.7'8

ISBN 0 0444 8142 X

Designed by Pete Lawrence
Illustrated by Oxford Illustrators
Typeset by Cambridge Photosetting Services
Printed in Great Britain by
Alden Press Ltd., Oxford
and bound by Hunter & Foules Ltd., Edinburgh

Teachers' guide

● ● ● ● ● ●

Introduction

The three books in this series constitute a wide-ranging collection of activities which involve children in the use of electronic calculators as a fundamental part of their mathematical education in the primary years. As the *National Curriculum Proposals* point out, 'it is essential that all pupils leave school knowing how to use a calculator effectively'. (*National Curriculum Proposals* para. 3.33; 1988.)

The series is designed to complement and be used as part of the existing mathematics scheme(s) of your school, and has a numerical and conceptual content that is closely matched to all the major mathematics schemes currently available. It is *not* a comprehensive scheme for the teaching of arithmetical skills and concepts through the use of calculators. Rather, it contains a series of activities, games, problems and investigations in which the calculator can be clearly seen to be an *aid* to the child in his or her learning. It is always possible for children to use pencil and paper to work out an arithmetical problem and, in fact, there are few curricular or 'real-world' situations in which a calculator is essential to the child. It is likely, therefore, that some children could work through almost all the pages in this series without recourse to a calculator! However, there are a number of benefits to be gained from calculator use at all stages of primary education.

1 There is immediate feedback to the child about the correctness or otherwise of his or her work. This important asset of calculator use can give many children increased confidence in their abilities. Related to this is the fact that early indication of mistakes can prevent their reinforcement as the child proceeds through a page or section of a scheme.

2 Calculators are a significant motivator for children of all ages. As in all school subjects and activities, there are some aspects of mathematics which are relatively tedious. The calculator can help to reduce the burden of routine computation and induce a more positive attitude to mathematics in general.

3 Related to the last point is the fact that the reduction in the burden of arithmetic can have a very beneficial effect on two aspects of work, namely the attention span of the child, which is always increased by the use of calculators, and the ability of the child to concentrate on the purpose of the activity with a reduced tendency to be side-tracked into 'number crunching'.

4 Proficiency with calculators allows the child to use realistic numbers reliably in problem solving. In this way the child's ability to estimate, round and approximate quantities can be greatly enhanced.

5 It is likely that the use of calculators will occasionally throw up a concept which is new to the child. Such situations might involve, for example, the production of a negative number or an interesting decimal in the display. The door is then open for you to discuss the concept in a context actually created by the child and therefore of significant interest to him or her.

6 Similar to the above is the situation which often arises in the use of calculators for the teaching of money. The classical example is the way in which the calculator will show 50p or £0·50 as 0.5 when producing this amount as the 'answer' in the display. Lack of understanding of the link may indicate a lack of understanding of place value, the notation of money, or both. These can then be explored further in a child-orientated context. The calculator can therefore be of significant use to the teacher as a tool of diagnosis, which is so essential in formative assessment and evaluation of learning.

Contents

CALCULATED TO PLEASE BOOK 2

	National Curriculum **Level 2**	National Curriculum **Level 3**	National Curriculum **Level 4**
AT 1 **Using and applying mathematics** Use number, algebra and measures in practical tasks, in real life problems, and to investigate within mathematics itself	• select the materials and the mathematics to use for a task. • describe current work, record findings and check results. • ask and respond to the question: 'What would happen if . . .?'	• select the materials and the mathematics to use for a task; check results and consider whether they are sensible. • explain work being done and record findings systematically. • make and test predictions.	• select the materials and the mathematics to use for a task; plan work methodically. • record findings and present them in oral, written or visual form as appropriate. • use examples to test statements or definitions.
	Calculated To Please Activities 1 2	**Calculated To Please Activities** 3 4 5 6 7 8 9 10 11 12 13 14 15 16 17 18 19	**Calculated To Please Activities** 20 21 22 23 24 25 26 27 28 29 30 31 32 33 34 35 36 37 38 39 40 41 42
AT 2 **Number** Understand number and number notation	• read, write and order numbers to at least 100; use the knowledge that the tens-digit indicates the number of tens. • understand the meaning of 'a half' and 'a quarter'.	• read, write and order numbers to at least 1000; use the knowledge that the position of a digit indicates its value. • use decimal notation as the conventional way of recording in money. • appreciate the meaning of negative whole numbers in familiar contexts.	• read, write and order whole numbers. • understand the effect of multiplying a whole number by 10 or 100. • use, with understanding, decimal notation to two decimal places in the context of measurement. • recognise and understand simple everyday fractions. • recognise and understand simple percentages. • understand and use the relationship between place values in whole numbers.
	Calculated To Please Activities 1 2	**Calculated To Please Activities** 3 4 5 6 7 8 9 10 11 12 13 14 15 16 17 18 19 24 25 26 27 29 31	**Calculated To Please Activities** 17 18 19 20 21 22 23 24 25 26 27 28 29 30 31 32 33 34 35 36 37 38 39 40 41 42
AT 3 **Number** Understand number operations (addition, subtraction, multiplication and division) and make use of appropriate methods of calculation	• know and use addition and subtraction facts up to 10. • compare two numbers to find the difference. • solve whole number problems involving addition and subtraction, including money.	• know and use addition and subtraction number facts to 20 (including zero). • solve problems involving multiplication or division of whole numbers or money, using a calculator where necessary. • know and use multiplication facts up to 5 × 5, and all those in 2, 5 and 10 multiplication tables.	• know multiplication facts up to 10 × 10 and use them in multiplication and division problems. • (using whole numbers) add or subtract mentally two 2-digit numbers; add mentally several single-digit numbers; without a calculator add and subtract two 3-digit numbers, multiply a 2-digit number by a single-digit number and divide a 2-digit number by a single-digit number. • solve addition or subtraction problems using numbers with no more than two decimal places; solve multiplication or division problems starting with whole numbers.
	Calculated To Please Activities 1	**Calculated To Please Activities** 1 2 3 4 5 6 7 8 9 10 11 12 13 14 15 16 26 29 34	**Calculated To Please Activities** 17 18 19 20 21 22 23 24 25 27 28 29 30 31 32 33 35 36 37 38 39 40 41 42

AT 4 **Number** Estimate and approximate in number	● make a sensible estimate of a number of objects up to 20.	● recognise that the first digit is the most important in indicating the size of a number, and approximate to the nearest 10 or 100. ● understand 'remainders' given the context of calculation, and know whether to round up or down.	● make use of estimation and approximation to check the validity of addition and subtraction calculations. ● read a calculator display to the nearest whole number. ● know how to interpret results on a calculator which have rounding errors.
	Calculated To Please Activities 1 2	**Calculated To Please Activities** 3 4 5 6 7 8 9 10 11 12 13 14 15 16 17 18 19 24 34	**Calculated To Please Activities** 6 7 8 10 11 12 13 14 15 16 17 18 19 20 21 22 23 24 25 26 27 28 29 30 31 32 33 35 36 37 38 39 40 41 42
AT 5 **Number/Algebra** Recognise and use patterns, relationships and sequences and make generalisations	● explore and use the patterns in addition and subtraction facts to 10. ● distinguish between odd and even numbers.	● explain number patterns and predict subsequent numbers where appropriate. ● find number patterns and equivalent forms of 2-digit numbers and use these to perform mental calculations. ● recognise whole numbers which are exactly divisible by 2, 5 and 10.	● apply strategies, such as doubling and halving, to explore properties of numbers, including equivalence of fractions. ● generalise, mainly in words, patterns which arise in various situations.
	Calculated To Please Activities 1 2	**Calculated To Please Activities** 1 2 3 4 5 6 7 8 9 10 11 12 13 14 15 16 17 18 19 24 26 29 34 37 38	**Calculated To Please Activities** 16 20 21 22 23 24 25 27 28 30 31 32 33 35 36 39 40 41 42
AT 6 **Algebra** Recognise and use functions, formulae, equations and inequalities	● understand the use of a symbol to stand for an unknown number.	● deal with inputs to and outputs from simple function machines.	● understand and use simple formulae or equations expressed in words. ● recognise that multiplication and division are inverse operations and use this to check calculations.
	Calculated to Please Activities 1 2 3	**Calculated To Please Activities** 2 3 4 5 6 7 8 9 10 11 12 13 14 15 16 17 18 19 24 25 26 29	**Calculated To Please Activities** 16 17 18 19 20 21 22 23 27 28 29 30 31 32 33 34 35 36 37 38 39 40 41 42

The target users of *Calculated to Please*

Calculated to Please is a series of three books, each containing about 40 activities.

Book 1 has been designed for use with children in the infant age range of 5 to 7 years. It concentrates on keyboard skills, general familiarity with the calculator, and work in addition and subtraction of whole numbers.

Book 2 has been designed for use with younger junior children between the ages of 7 and 9 years. It concentrates on general arithmetical work with whole numbers, including the skills of estimation, simply investigations and items of problem solving.

Book 3 has been designed for use with older junior or middle-school children between the ages of 9 and 12 years. It concentrates on the wider application of calculator skills as tools of investigation and problem solving, with a particular emphasis on work on decimals and the associated concepts. Work on the calculator memory and some of the general functions of a calculator are also included.

Each book has been closely related to the content of mainstream mathematics schemes. However, the provision of materials also takes account of the fact that children using calculators, once they are familiar with the basic operations, are able to work at a slightly higher arithmetical level than the mainstream schemes would seem to suggest. Each of the books, therefore, concentrates on the *processes* of arithmetical and mathematical thinking and activity rather than on purely numerical manipulation. This reflects directly the *National Curriculum Proposals* which, in paragraph 3.33 state: 'Using a calculator effectively depends on an understanding of the number operations to be performed on the calculator, an estimate of the expected answer, a correct sequence of operations on the keyboard, and an intelligent interpretation of the results.' All these aspects are included in *Calculated to Please*.

Using *Calculated to Please*

In all three books, each of the photocopyable sheets for the children is linked to a page of teachers' notes. Together, these teachers' pages form a comprehensive set of notes designed to:

- help teachers to see the purpose of each activity;
- indicate clearly the level of mathematical skill required of the child;
- suggest additional equipment which is essential, or at least useful, to each activity;
- indicate ways in which each page might be used with a group or individual;

- suggest, where appropriate, further activities, discussion or extensions to the work done.
- provide answers to the questions on the children's pages or indicate likely solutions;

A single class contains children with a wide range of aptitudes, abilities and attitudes and the material can be used flexibly to match these various needs. The single-page format allows individuals or groups to work at different levels and on different topics, according to the wishes of the teacher.

Why do you need *Calculated to Please?*

Your school probably has a single commercially produced scheme, or a school-based scheme which integrates several published resources. Such schemes vary considerably in quality and provision of materials and few have made a serious effort to provide suitable calculator activities for children. Similarly, few have made a serious effort to provide materials which can be used to match children's individual needs.

Calculated to Please has been written to provide a flexible resource for busy teachers. It can be

integrated with a mainstream scheme if desired, or retained as the basis of a calculator course for children. Ideally it would be used to provide children with extra general motivational activities, which themselves develop some of the more important mental resources to enable children to deal more effectively with their current and future mathematical learning. Thus a measure of integration, combined with specific use as a topic on 'calculators', would seem to be the best mode of working with the materials.

Choosing a calculator

There is a vast range of calculators on the market, many of which are suitable for use in primary classrooms. Many children possess their own calculators which should be examined carefully to assess their suitability for primary-school use. It would be useful to check with the Local Education Authority before making a bulk purchase of calculators for a school.

One aspect of choice which can be of particular importance is that of the 'logic' of the calculator, that is, its ability to operate on the numbers in the order in which they are entered into the calculator by the user. There is a clear choice to be made in the mode of operation of the calculator. Two types are available.

Arithmetic logic will produce the following:

| 3 | + | 4 | × | 5 | = | | *35.* |

That is, the calculation is carried out in the order of entry of the numbers and operations.

Algebraic logic will produce the following:

| 3 | + | 4 | × | 5 | = | | *23.* |

That is, the calculation gives priority to the operations of multiplication (and division). This is *algebraically* correct, but can cause problems for younger children who have not met the use of brackets. However, such a calculator will conform to the 'order of entry' mode if the user presses:

| 3 | + | 4 | = | × | 5 | = | | *35.* |

That is, the equals key is pressed to 'lock in' the first part of the calculation before proceeding. Alternatively, the memory can be used to the same effect.

Most primary school calculators use arithmetic logic. All advanced or scientific calculators use algebraic logic.

Assessment of progress

Because a calculator is purely a tool, and not an end in itself, assessment can be made on a more flexible basis than is the case with the mainstream mathematics curriculum. Use of a calculator is not amenable to formal testing, but is part of the general process of mathematical activity.

Assessment should therefore be *formative*, that is to say, it should be concerned with how well the child is learning. The aims of assessment in this area should be:

- to help children to see what you expect of them;
- to help you, as the teacher, to use the materials of the 'course' more effectively;
- to allow useful interaction between teacher and child;
- to encourage children to respond positively and creatively to calculators in the classroom;
- to provide rapid feedback to the child about progress;
- to allow you to diagnose weakness.

To aid the assessment and record keeping of children's progress in calculator use, a checklist of selected items of appropriate knowledge, skills and attitudes is included in this book on the next six pages. The fifty items on the checklist are not meant to be an exhaustive survey, but rather to indicate the range and sequence of development in a child's ability to use, and his or her degree of acceptance of, calculators as a major force in present and future mathematical learning.

It should be noted that items 41 to 50 require a judgement from you about the degree of 'appropriateness' of children's responses. They are general aspects of calculator use which can be considered at all levels of work. They are subdivisions of what was referred to in the HMI/DES document *Mathematics 5–16* as 'the sensible use of a calculator'.

A sequence of content and skill objectives related to calculator use

Name _____

Class _____

1 Experience and use of the ON/OFF switch.

2 Experience of the calculator display numerals.

3 Experience of the calculator keyboard numerals.

4 Matching of the keyboard numerals and calculator display numerals.

5 Matching of printed, handwritten, keyboard and display numerals.

6 Experience of the operation keys of addition and subtraction.

7 Experience of the 'equals' key.

8 Recognition and use of $\boxed{C}$, $\boxed{CE}$ or $\boxed{C/CE}$ keys to clear the calculator and display.

9 Use of the calculator to create and check one-step addition bonds;
   (a) to 10   E.g. $\boxed{C}\boxed{3}\boxed{+}\boxed{4}\boxed{=}$ $\boxed{\qquad\qquad 7.}$
   (b) to 20.

A sequence of content and skill objectives related to calculator use

Name ——

Class ——

10 Use of the calculator to create and check two-step addition bonds;

    (a) to 10   E.g. $\boxed{C}\,\boxed{1}\,\boxed{+}\,\boxed{2}\,\boxed{+}\,\boxed{3}\,\boxed{=}$ $\boxed{\qquad\qquad\qquad\qquad 6.}$

    (b) to 20.

11 Use of the calculator to create and check one-step subtraction bonds;

    (a) to 10   (b) to 20.

12 Given an unfinished equation, to choose the operation key $\boxed{+}$ or $\boxed{-}$ to create a display number less than 20.

13 Extension of addition and subtraction calculator skills to numbers less than 100, through puzzles and investigations.

14 Use of a calculator to check and illustrate the inverse nature of the processes of addition and subtraction.

15 Experience and use of the constant function of the calculator.

16 Experience of multiplication as repeated addition, using a calculator to illustrate the process.

A sequence of content and skill objectives related to calculator use

Name _____

Class _____

17 Use of the calculator to create and check multiplication bonds.

18 Experience of division as repeated subtraction, using a calculator to illustrate the process.

19 Use of a calculator in simple chain calculations involving combinations of the four operations of addition, subtraction, multiplication and division.

20 Appropriate use of a calculator to check simple estimation skills based on rounding numbers.

21 Use of a calculator to create 'upside-down' words as a reinforcement of keyboard skills.

22 Use of a calculator to *continue* a given number pattern or sequence.

23 Use of a calculator to *complete* a given number pattern or sequence by finding the missing numbers.

24 Use of a calculator to *create* simple number patterns.

A sequence of content and skill objectives related to calculator use

Name _____

Class _____

25 Experience of the decimal point on the calculator.

26 Use of the calculator in 'decimal' place value situations.

27 Use of a calculator in money computations.

28 Use of a calculator in length computations.

29 Use of a calculator in area computations.

30 Use of a calculator in mass computations.

31 Use of a calculator in volume and capacity computations.

32 Use of a calculator in time and speed computations.

33 Use of the calculator memory keys in chain computations.

34 Use of a calculator in ordering fractions.

A sequence of content and skill objectives related to calculator use

Name _____

Class _____

35 Use of a calculator in matching fractions and decimals.

36 Recognition and use of the $\boxed{\%}$ key.

37 Recognition and use of the $\boxed{+/-}$ key.

38 Recognition and use of the $\boxed{x^2}$ key.

39 Recognition and use of the $\boxed{\sqrt{}}$ key.

40 Recognition and use of the $\boxed{1/x}$ key.

The following are more general aspects of calculator experience and use, which can be considered at all levels of children's work.

41 Appropriate use of the calculator for checking answers or estimates.

42 Appropriate use of the calculator to generate a large number of examples to aid generalisation of rules.

A sequence of content and skill objectives related to calculator use

Name _____

Class _____

43 Appropriate use of the calculator to reduce the burden of calculation when using large numbers.

44 Appropriate use of the calculator to play games specifically designed for calculator involvement.

45 Appropriate use of a calculator to play general number games.

46 Appropriate observation and discussion of 'new' concepts arising from calculator use, e.g. negative numbers.

47 Appropriate use of the calculator in the application of mathematics to the environment.

48 Appropriate use of the calculator in mathematical investigations.

49 Appropriate use of calculators across the curriculum, e.g. in science, history, geography and environmental/social studies.

50 Development of a sensible attitude to the existence, use and potential of calculators in school work and in everyday life.

Ghostbusters!

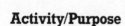

Activity/Purpose

The activity is a simple investigation of the different totals which can be achieved by finding sums of any three of a restricted set of given numbers.

The given set of numbers is 11 to 19 inclusive. The child finds the highest and lowest totals and records them. The seventeen other possible totals are then listed, after checking using a calculator.

Previous mathematical knowledge and skill required

Experience of addition of number.
Familiarity with the keyboard technique for addition of two-digit numbers.

Notes on using the page

Check the child's understanding of the activity and of the terms 'highest', 'lowest' and 'total'.
Ensure that the child uses only *three* numbers at one time.
Encourage the child to use a system to find the other totals, or some may be omitted.

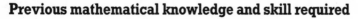

Answers/Solutions

Highest total is $17 + 18 + 19 = 54$.
Lowest total is $11 + 12 + 13 = 36$.
17 other totals (37 to 53 inclusive) are possible.

EQUIPMENT

 Calculator.

ADDITIONAL ACTIVITIES EXTENSIONS

1. Discuss the commutativity of addition, i.e.
   $11 + 12 + 13 = 13 + 12 + 11$.
2. Encourage the child to record some of the means of achieving the other totals and therefore to observe that, for example:

$$42 = 11 + 12 + 19$$
$$= 11 + 13 + 18$$
$$= 12 + 13 + 17$$
$$= 13 + 14 + 15$$

 Ⓝ Ⓞ Ⓣ Ⓔ Ⓢ

Links with our own maths scheme

Other activities and extensions used

General evaluation of the children's work

Ghostbusters

The ghostbusters can zap any **3** ghosts at a time!

The **highest** total that can be zapped is $\square + \square + \square = \diamond$

The **lowest** total that can be zapped is $\bigcirc + \bigcirc + \bigcirc = \bigcirc$

Write the other totals that can be zapped!

Name _____   **Class** _____

ADDITION USING A CALCULATOR.

© Unwin Hyman
Calculated to Please 2

Sure-shot ②

● ● ● ● ● ●

Activity/Purpose

The activity is a simple investigation of ways to achieve given target numbers using a restricted number of keys. It relates directly to the skills and knowledge developed in *Book 1*.

In the first six questions, selected keys are 'given' to aid understanding; in the last four questions the responses are more open.
Mental arithmetic skills and estimation skills are likely to be used in this activity.

Previous mathematical knowledge and skill required

Awareness of the concepts of addition and subtraction.
Keyboard skills as developed in *Book 1*.

Notes on using the page

Check first the child's awareness of the meaning of *addition* and *subtraction* and that he/she can distinguish between the symbols and . Stress the need to 'clear' the calculator after each attempt, by pressing or .
If possible *check* the answers to the first six examples before the child moves on to the more open-ended questions. Stress that the aim is to use *as few keys as possible*.

● ● ● ● ● ●

Answers/Solutions

1. 3−3=0
2. 3+3=6
3. 3+5=8
4. 5+5=10

5. 5−3=2
6. 5−5=0 *or*
   3−3=0
7. 3+3+3=9

8. 3+3+3+5=14
9. 3+3+3−5=4 *or*
   5+5−3−3=4
10. 3+3+5=11

○ Ⓝ Ⓞ Ⓣ Ⓔ Ⓢ

Links with our own maths scheme

Other activities and extensions used

General evaluation of the children's work

EQUIPMENT

 Calculator.

ADDITIONAL ACTIVITIES EXTENSIONS

1. Encourage two children to compare 'answers' and discuss
   (a) numbers of keys pressed;
   (b) differences between 'answers' (e.g. is 3+5+3+3 different to 5+3+3+3?).

2. Encourage investigation of other targets under 20, using the given keys, e.g.:
   1=3+3−5
   18=5+5+5+3

The first unnumbered blank at the back of the book can be used for this; or for exercises with other number keys of your choice, to suit individual needs.

Use only these keys ⟶ [c] [3] [5] [+] [–] [=]
on this sheet.

Fill in the keys you press to get the answer in the display.

1. [3] [ ] [ ] [=] | 0.
2. [ ] [+] [ ] [=] | 6.
3. [ ] [ ] [5] [=] | 8.
4. [ ] [ ] [ ] [ ] | 10.
5. [ ] [ ] [ ] [ ] | 2.
6. [ ] [–] [ ] [ ] | 0.

Press [c] before each try!

Now do these. Make each target number.
Use as few keys as you can!
Write your answers in the boxes next to the targets.

7. **9** ↔

8. **14** ↔

9. **4** ↔

10. **11** ↔

Name _____   Class _____

© Unwin Hyman
Calculated to Please 2

Number slimmer 1, 2 and 3

 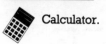

③–⑤

PLACE VALUE AND
ESTIMATION.
SUBTRACTING 1, 10, 100

Activity/Purpose

The purpose of the activity is to use a calculator to reinforce the child's understanding of place value, and to encourage the development of estimation skills in 'reading' the relative values of large numbers.

Given a starting number, the child uses a mental method to make a 'good guess' of the answer when either one, ten or one hundred is subtracted. The guess is then checked using a calculator and the work is 'marked' immediately by the child.

Previous mathematical knowledge and skill required

Experience of place value is a concept and its application to hundreds, tens and units in our base-10 system.
Some knowledge of how to set up and use a subtraction constant in the calculator is desirable.

Notes on using the pages

First of all discuss briefly the techniques of counting on and back by a constant amount. If possible, refer to activities 37 and 38 *Step up* and *Count down* in *Calculated to Please Book 1*.
Ensure that the child makes his or her 'good guess' *before* using the calculator to check.

Allow use of either of these techniques.

(a) $\boxed{C}$ (number) $\boxed{-}$ $\boxed{1}\boxed{0}$ $\boxed{=}$
   N.B. $\boxed{C}$ should be pressed
   after each attempt

or **(b)** (setting the constant)
   $\boxed{1}\boxed{0}$ $\boxed{-}$ $\boxed{-}$ $\boxed{=}$ $\boxed{0}$
   then (number) $\boxed{=}$
   N.B. there is no need
   to press $\boxed{C}$
   between
   attempts

EQUIPMENT

 Calculator.

ADDITIONAL ACTIVITIES EXTENSIONS

1. A consistent problem with these pages indicates a need for the child to return to structured apparatus to develop a proper understanding of place value.

2. Discuss the patterns which emerge as the numbers are diminished by the given amount, e.g.:

    $511-10= 501$
    $1111-10=1101$
    $2101-10=2091$

   In the first two examples only the last two digits change. In the third example, the tens and units digits together total less than 10, so the hundreds column must be altered too.

3. An unnumbered blank of this page is supplied at the back of the book for further practice with numbers of your choice.

Answers/Solutions

Sheet 1: 96, 100, 110, 199, 378, 219, 998, 1000, 1009, 1999, 5079, 1110, 9999

Sheet 2: 90, 224, 193, 389, 501, 960, 1101, 2198, 2091, 7756, 8893, 9991, 10091

Sheet 3: 10, 190, 888, 1, 900, 1910, 2001, 1979, 4344, 1011, 7554, 9901, 10000

○ Ⓝ ⓞ Ⓣ Ⓔ Ⓢ

Number Slimmer 1 ③

Take **one unit** from each of these numbers.
Write down a **good guess** at the answer *before* you use a calculator!

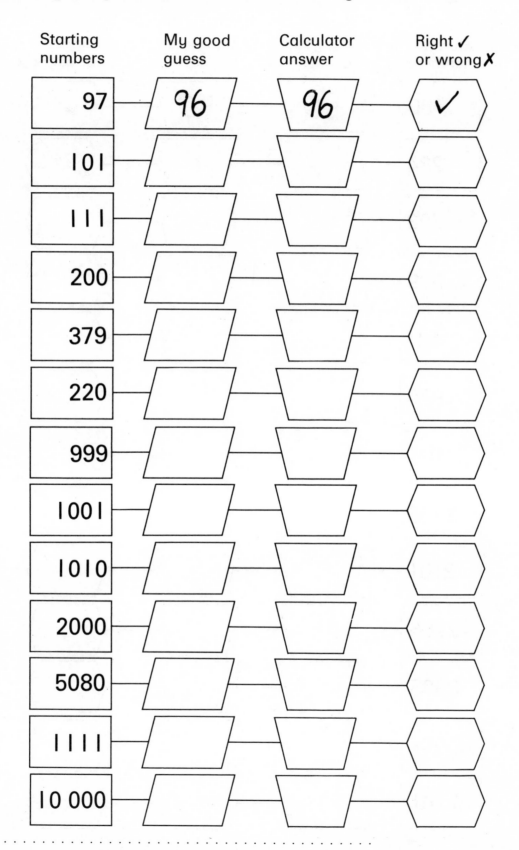

Starting numbers	My good guess	Calculator answer	Right ✓ or wrong ✗
97	96	96	✓
101			
111			
200			
379			
220			
999			
1001			
1010			
2000			
5080			
11111			
10 000			

Name _____ Class _____

PLACE VALUE AND ESTIMATION PRACTICE (SUBTRACTING 1).

© Unwin Hyman
Calculated to Please 2

Number Slimmer 2

Take **a ten** from each of these numbers.
Write down a **good guess** at the answer *before* you use a calculator!

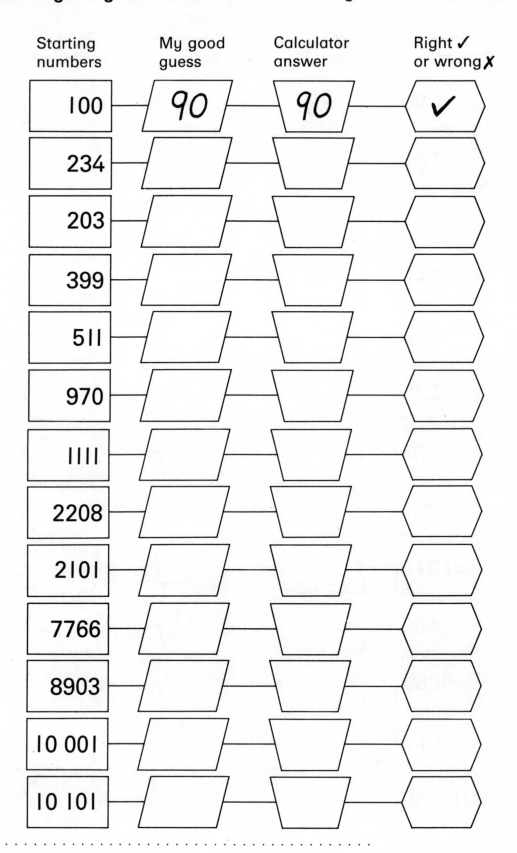

Starting numbers	My good guess	Calculator answer	Right ✓ or wrong ✗
100	90	90	✔
234			
203			
399			
511			
970			
1111			
2208			
2101			
7766			
8903			
10 001			
10 101			

Name _____   Class _____

PLACE VALUE AND ESTIMATION PRACTICE (SUBTRACTING 10).

© Unwin Hyman
Calculated to Please 2

Number Slimmer 3 ⑤ ●●●●●●●

Take **a hundred** from each of these numbers.
Write down a **good guess** at the answer *before* you use a calculator!

Starting numbers	My good guess	Calculator answer	Right ✓ or wrong ✗
110	10	10	✓
290			
988			
101			
1000			
2010			
2101			
2079			
4444			
1111			
7654			
10 001			
10 100			

Name _____   Class _____

PLACE VALUE AND ESTIMATION PRACTICE (SUBTRACTING 100).

© Unwin Hyman
Calculated to Please 2

Multiplying

Activity/Purpose

The purpose is to introduce to the child the basic technique of setting up and using a calculator for multiplication. A series of multiplication calculations is presented in horizontal form. The child fills in the answers in the 'display' spaces, in normal handwriting. Multiplication of one-digit and two-digit numbers is included.

Previous mathematical knowledge and skill required

Awareness of the concept of multiplication. Some knowledge of the technique of multiplication is useful. Multiplication cannot be *taught* using a calculator; the purpose of the activity is to show how quite difficult calculations can be done almost instantaneously, provided the correct sequence is used and an estimate of the answer is already in the child's head.

Notes on using the page

Check first that the child is able to understand the nature of multiplication as a short-hand method for repeated addition of equal amounts. Some experience of the use of the constant function for addition would help in discussion of how multiples are created.

Stress the need to clear the calculator before each question, by pressing C or C/CE. As was found in *Book 1* with addition and subtraction, some of the calculations are capable of easy mental solution. Encourage the use of non-calculator methods when suitable, to avoid reliance on mechanical means.

Answers/Solutions

A				**B**		**C**	
1. 12	**6.** 25			**1.** 48		**1.** 0	
2. 15	**7.** 35			**2.** 54		**2.** 30	
3. 21	**8.** 24			**3.** 80		**3.** 0	
4. 36	**9.** 24			**4.** 16		**4.** 38	
5. 27	**10.** 36			**5.** 0		**5.** 90	

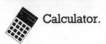

EQUIPMENT

Calculator.

ADDITIONAL ACTIVITIES EXTENSIONS

1. Encourage the child to create 'strings' of multiplication calculations on 1 cm squared paper. Insist that the calculations are recorded and worked through to an 'answer'.

2. Encourage the use of larger numbers by able children.

3. Discuss the need to read the whole question first. For example, in questions B5, C1 and C3 the multiplication by zero indicates a zero product and the rest of the keyed items become unnecessary. Similarly, multiplication by 1 need not be keyed in.

N O T E S

Multiplying

Fill the display boxes. Check each answer using your calculator.

A

keys	display		keys	display
1. C 2 × 6 =		6.	C 5 × 5 =	
2. C 3 × 5 =		7.	C 7 × 5 =	
3. C 7 × 3 =		8.	C 8 × 3 =	
4. C 6 × 6 =		9.	C 4 × 6 =	
5. C 9 × 3 =		10.	C 9 × 4 =	

B

keys   display

1. C 2 × 3 × 2 × 4 =
2. C 3 × 3 × 3 × 2 =
3. C 4 × 2 × 5 × 2 =
4. C 2 × 2 × 2 × 2 =
5. C 1 × 9 × 6 × 0 =

Always press C before you start.

C

keys   display

1. C 10 × 7 × 0 =
2. C 15 × 1 × 2 =
3. C 0 × 99 × 2 =
4. C 1 × 2 × 19 =
5. C 3 × 3 × 10 =

Name _____ Class _____

MULTIPLICATION OF ONE-DIGIT AND TWO-DIGIT NUMBERS.

© Unwin Hyman
Calculated to Please 2

On the wing ⑦

● ● ● ● ● ●

Activity/Purpose

The basic purpose of the colouring activity is to reinforce the skill of keying in a multiplication calculation, using calculations presented horizontally in the normal printed style. The child uses a calculator, or a written or mental method, to complete the multiplication sentences. If a non-calculator method is employed, then the calculator should be used to check the answer. Each answer is related to a colour, as shown on the sheet. The child colours the spaces and shapes according to the given colour code. A symmetrical picture emerges which contains six different plane shapes.

Previous mathematical knowledge and skill required

Awareness of the concept of multiplication. Experience of the work on the previous page.

Notes on using the page

Make sure that the child has used the previous page, *Multiplying*. Remind the child to press C or C/CE before each calculation. Point out that the calculator should be used only if the calculation cannot be worked out easily in another way.

● ● ● ● ● ●

Answers/Solutions

		Left	Right
Upper wing	purple	49	45
Lower wing	pink	0	32
Ellipse (oval)	green	42	0
Hexagon	blue	60	24
Triangle (isosceles)	yellow	54	80
Parallelogram	orange	27	36
Circle	red	72	81
Pentagon	brown	99	64

Ⓝ Ⓞ Ⓣ Ⓔ Ⓢ

EQUIPMENT

 Calculator.

 Coloured pencils.

 Shapes template.

ADDITIONAL ACTIVITIES EXTENSIONS

1. Discuss the symmetry of the shape which has emerged.

2. Encourage the drawing of another butterfly or other symmetrical pattern which incorporates some of the named plane shapes and other plane shapes as well. Use of a shapes template as recommended.

3. Discuss the special problem associated with multiplication by zero.

On the wing

⑦ ●●●●●●●

Use your calculator to find the answers to the calculations in the picture.

Then use this code to colour the shapes and spaces.

Left-hand side	
Answers	**Colour**
72	red
54	yellow
42	green
27	orange
60	blue
99	brown
49	purple
0	pink

Right-hand side	
Answers	**Colour**
36	orange
80	yellow
24	blue
64	brown
81	red
45	purple
32	pink
0	green

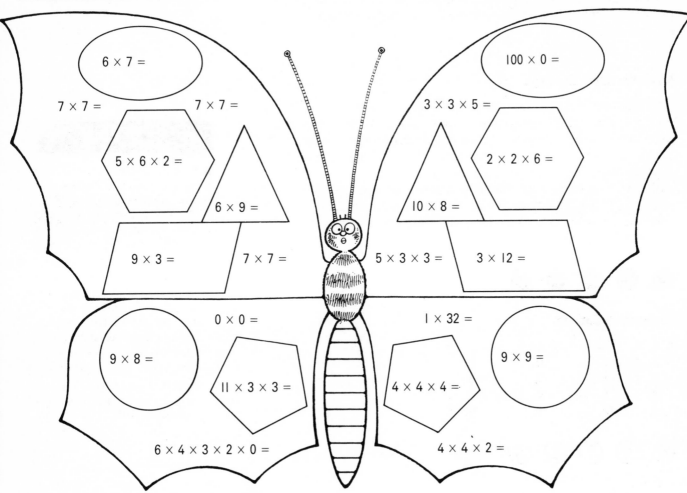

List the 6 **different** plane shapes you can see.

1. _____ 2. _____ 3. _____

4. _____ 5. _____ 6. _____

Name _____ Class _____

MULTIPLICATION PUZZLE.

© Unwin Hyman
Calculated to Please 2

Dividing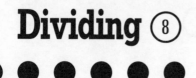

Activity/Purpose

The purpose is to introduce to the child the basic technique of
setting up and using a calculator for division. A series of division
calculations is presented in horizontal form. The child fills in the
answers in the display spaces, in normal handwriting. The
multiplication of one-digit and two-digit numbers is included.

Previous mathematical knowledge and skill required

Awareness of the concept of division (sharing *and* grouping).
Some knowledge of the technique of division is useful, since it
cannot be *taught* using a calculator. The purpose of the activity is
to show how a calculator removes the tedious aspect of division by
producing almost instantaneous answers; it emphasises how to
key in a sequence.

Notes on using the page

Check first that the child has experience of the technique of
division, using structural apparatus and pencil-and-paper
methods. Some experience of the use of the constant function for
subtraction would help to show how division 'counts back' equal-
sized amounts.
Stress the need to clear the calculator before each question by
pressing C or C/CE. Foster the use of non-calculator methods
where appropriate. Encourage the child to estimate the answer
before using the calculator.

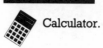

EQUIPMENT

Calculator.

ADDITIONAL ACTIVITIES EXTENSIONS

N.B. Open-minded activities using
division are unsuitable at this stage
because they so often require
explanation of decimals. Much more
important is discussion of the links
between ÷ and ×, and between
÷ and −.

1. ÷ and ×. Encourage the child
   to begin with the display number
   and use × to achieve the
   starting number. Discuss the
   inverse/reciprocal nature of the
   process.

2. ÷ and −. Encourage the child
   to use − instead of ÷, to
   achieve the display number by
   successive subtraction.

Answers/Solutions

A				**B**		**C**	
1.	2	**6.**	6	**1.** 6		**1.**	3
2.	4	**7.**	2	**2.** 1		**2.**	1
3.	1	**8.**	4	**3.** 4		**3.**	2
4.	2	**9.**	3	**4.** 3		**4.**	1
5.	3	**10.**	1	**5.** 1		**5.**	25

N O T E S

Dividing

Fill the display boxes. Check each answer using your calculator.

A

	keys	display		keys	display
1.	C 4 ÷ 2 =		6.	C 6 ÷ 1 =	
2.	C 4 ÷ 1 =		7.	C 8 ÷ 4 =	
3.	C 4 ÷ 4 =		8.	C 8 ÷ 2 =	
4.	C 6 ÷ 3 =		9.	C 9 ÷ 3 =	
5.	C 6 ÷ 2 =		10.	C 7 ÷ 7 =	

B

keys   display

1. C 1 2 ÷ 2 ÷ 1 =
2. C 1 5 ÷ 3 ÷ 5 =
3. C 2 0 ÷ 1 ÷ 5 =
4. C 1 8 ÷ 3 ÷ 2 =
5. C 2 5 ÷ 5 ÷ 5 =

Always press C before you start.

C

keys   display

1. C 2 7 ÷ 3 ÷ 3 =
2. C 1 ÷ 1 ÷ 1 ÷ 1 =
3. C 3 0 ÷ 3 ÷ 5 =
4. C 1 9 ÷ 1 9 ÷ 1 =
5. C 1 0 0 ÷ 4 =

Name _____ Class _____

DIVISION OF ONE-DIGIT AND TWO-DIGIT NUMBERS.

© Unwin Hyman
Calculated to Please 2

Catch a code! ⑨

● ● ● ● ● ●

Activity/Purpose

The basic purpose of the activity is to reinforce the skill of keying in division calculations using calculations presented in normal printed form. The child uses a calculator, or a written or mental method where appropriate, to find the answers to the division calculations. These are then matched with the coded number/ letter combinations, to give the sentence 'Who is your best friend?'. The child writes the answer in code in the space provided. A further code is given, of the word calculator, the child decodes this and draws his or her own calculator.

Previous mathematical knowledge and skill required

Awareness of the concept of division. Experience of the work on the previous page.

Notes on using the page

Remind the child to clear the calculator before each calculation. Given the experience of the previous page, the calculations can be attempted by the child working alone; they will produce a self-checking response.
Allow the name of the friend to be 'written' in a way which matches the ability of the child; i.e. more able children should be encouraged to use division calculations, whereas the less able may only manage the fixed number/letter code.

● ● ● ● ● ●

Answers/Solutions

As discussed above.

EQUIPMENT

 Calculator.

 Ruler.

 Possibly coloured pencils.

ADDITIONAL ACTIVITIES EXTENSIONS

1. The child can invent a different code and use it to form words for a friend to decode.

2. Once the calculator has been drawn, the keys can be coloured in to show the different types and their purposes. (Refer to *Book 1* for a simpler activity for less able or younger children.)

3. Encourage the child to check calculations by multiplying the display number by the divisor.

Ⓝ Ⓞ Ⓣ Ⓔ Ⓢ

Links with our own maths scheme

Other activities and extensions used

General evaluation of the children's work

Catch a code !

This is **your** secret code.

Vowels				
A	E	I	O	U
1	2	3	4	5

Curvy letters								
B	C	D	G	J	P	Q	R	S
6	7	8	9	10	11	12	13	14

Straight letters											
F	H	K	L	M	N	T	V	W	X	Y	Z
15	16	17	18	19	20	21	22	23	24	25	26

Use your calculator to decode the message.

Code	69 ÷ 3	64 ÷ 4	60 ÷ 15	27 ÷ 9	56 ÷ 4
Letters	W	☐	☐	☐	☐

Code	75 ÷ 3	28 ÷ 7	75 ÷ 15	52 ÷ 4	30 ÷ 5	50 ÷ 25	42 ÷ 3	63 ÷ 3
Letters	☐	☐	☐	☐	☐	☐	☐	☐

Code	60 ÷ 4	65 ÷ 5	60 ÷ 20	20 ÷ 10	100 ÷ 5	72 ÷ 9
Letters	☐	☐	☐	☐	☐	☐ ?

Write the answer **in code** here.

Draw a

49 ÷ 7	☐	90 ÷ 5	☐
50 ÷ 50	☐	15 ÷ 15	☐
72 ÷ 4	☐	84 ÷ 4	☐
84 ÷ 12	☐	68 ÷ 17	☐
60 ÷ 12	☐	91 ÷ 7	☐ in this space.

Name _____ Class _____

CODE PUZZLE USING DIVISION OF WHOLE NUMBERS.

© Unwin Hyman
Calculated to Please 2

Times up!

Activity/Purpose

The activity is an introductory investigation into the factors of given numbers, and therefore is an introduction to tests of divisibility. It illustrates the inverse reciprocal relationship of multiplication and division since, to decide on the multiple of the given digit, a child must first divide.

Previous mathematical knowledge and skill required

Experience of the concepts of multiplication and division. Familiarity with zero.

Notes on using the page

Since all the numbers (except zero) can be transformed into 100 if use of decimals is allowed, it is essential to stress that the factor multiplied by the given number must itself be a *whole number*. Insist that the child shows how each decision was made.

Answers/Solutions

0	no	
1	yes	100×1
2	yes	50×2
3	no	
4	yes	25×4
5	yes	20×5
6	no	
7	no	
8	no	
9	no	
10	yes	10×10

EQUIPMENT

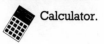 Calculator.

ADDITIONAL ACTIVITIES EXTENSIONS

Two unnumbered blanks of the page are supplied at the back of the book.

1. One of these allows other *target numbers* to be examined, e.g. even, odd, prime, larger than 100, and so on, and uses the digital form of the starting numbers 1 to 10.

2. The second allows other *starting numbers* to be examined, e.g. between 11 and 20, or multiples of 3, or prime numbers.

3. Look for and discuss any patterns which emerge, e.g. all even targets are divisible by 2; all targets ending in zero are divisible by 10.

See also Activities 37–39 *Equal shares and no spares*.

Links with our own maths scheme

Other activities and extensions used

General evaluation of the children's work

Times up!

Work out which of these numbers can be changed to | 100. | by multiplying by a **whole** number.

Use your calculator!

Number	Yes or No	Show how here!
0		
1		
2	Yes	2 x 50 = 100 50 x 2 = 100
3		
4		
5		
6		
7		
8		
9		
10		

If you have time, try some other numbers....

Name _____   Class _____

NUMBER INVESTIGATION. INTRODUCTION TO TESTS OF DIVISIBILITY.

© Unwin Hyman
Calculated to Please 2

Lift off!  ⑪

● ● ● ● ● ●

Activity/Purpose

The activity consists of a game for two players, who each aim to be the first to colour the rocket and therefore achieve Lift Off! Rules are provided on the game sheet.

The purposes of the activity are:
- to develop awareness of the constant function for multiplication by 2;
- to encourage the use of *estimation* skills in deciding which number to key in to the calculator;
- to highlight the inverse relationship of multiplication and division.

Previous mathematical knowledge and skill required

Awareness of multiplication tables. Experience of even/odd numbers. Awareness of the constant functions for addition and subtraction (see *Book 1*).

Notes on using the page

Ensure that the game rules are understood.
It is important that the children have some previous experience of the constant functions for addition and subtraction. **N.B.** The constant function for *addition* of 2 causes the calculator to 'count on' in twos. The constant function for *multiplication* produces numbers of which 2 is a factor. It does **not** produce the 2-times table or table of twos; instead it doubles each previous input or display. Stress that once the constant function is set into the calculator by pressing $\boxed{2}\,\boxed{\times}\,\boxed{\times}\,\boxed{=}\,\boxed{0}$, there is no need to clear the calculator each time a new entry is made. In fact if $\boxed{C}$ is pressed, the constant function is *removed* from the calculator and has to be reset.

● ● ● ● ●

Answers/Solutions

See above.

○ Ⓝ ⓞ Ⓣ Ⓔ Ⓢ

ADDITIONAL ACTIVITIES EXTENSIONS

1. Encourage discussion of the concepts of even numbers and factors and the quality of the children's estimates (measured by the number of 'goes' needed to complete a rocket).

2. If the child is capable, discuss the consequences of repeated pressing of $\boxed{=}$ after the constant has been set, i.e. 2, 4, 8, 16, 32, 64, 128, . . . It is important to be brief at this stage.

3. Encourage the child to redesign the game using *even* numbers on the rocket, between 200 and 500. Use the page opposite to make a unnumbered blank for this, or for numbers of your choice to suit individual needs.

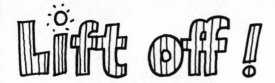 **Lift off !**

A game for 2 players.
Share **one** calculator.

Set the calculator for **multiply by 2** like this:

Press ⨂ ⨂ ⨂ ⨂ ⨂ .

Take turns.   Choose any number.
Key it into the calculator.

Then press ⬛ .

If the display number is on **your** rocket, colour it in.
The first to colour the whole rocket is the winner!

52	84
96	34
16	8
112	66
44	28
72	102

68	18
42	116
104	74
36	6
94	56
82	24

Name _____   Name _____

GAME USING THE CONSTANT FUNCTION FOR MULTIPLICATION BY 2.

Fly the flag!

Activity/Purpose

The activity consists of a game for two players, who each aim to be the first to colour a flag. Rules are provided on the game sheet.

The purposes of the activity are:
- to develop proficiency in using the constant function for multiplication;
- to encourage the use of estimation skills in the choice of numbers upon which to operate the constant;
- to emphasise the relationship between multiplication and division.

Previous mathematical knowledge and skill required

Awareness of multiplication bonds. Ability to label numbers as odd or even. Use of the previous activity *Lift-off!* is desirable before working on this page.

Notes on using the page

Reading of the notes on the previous page *Lift-off!* is essential. With that experience, the page should be self-explanatory.

Answers/Solutions

See above.

EQUIPMENT

 Calculator.

 A variety of coloured pencils or felt-tips.

ADDITIONAL ACTIVITIES EXTENSIONS

1. Discuss the quality of the estimates, measured by the number of attempts needed to find one of the multiples shown on the flags.

2. Discuss the fact that some numbers on the flags are odd and some are even.

3. Briefly discuss the facts which produce a divisibility by 3 (e.g. the sum of the digits is divisible by 3).

4. Encourage the child to examine the consequences of reversing the digits of all the numbers shown, (e.g. 135 becomes 531, which is also divisible by 3!).

5. Encourage the child to design a flag on which all the multiples of 3 are between 150 and 300. Use the page opposite to make an unnumbered blank for this, or for other numbers of your choice.

Links with our own maths scheme

Other activities and extensions used

General evaluation of the children's work

Fly the flag !

A game for 2 players.
Share **one** calculator.

Set the calculator for **multiply by 3** like this:

Press ⬚3 ⬚× ⬚× ⬚= ⬚0 .

Take turns. Choose any number.
Key it into the calculator.

Then press ⬚= .

If the display number is on **your** flag, colour it in.
The first to colour the whole flag is the winner!

39	84	15
135	111	72
57	9	102
27	150	42

51	108	18
87	75	123
45	114	21
6	36	81

Name _____   Name _____

GAME USING THE CONSTANT FUNCTION FOR MULTIPLICATION BY 3.

Join four today! ⑬

●　●　●　●　●　●

Activity/Purpose

The activity consists of a game for two players. The aim is to be the first player to have four counters in a horizontal, vertical or diagonal line. Rules are provided on the game sheet.

The purposes of the activities are:
- to develop awareness of the constant function for division by 2, i.e. halving any chosen number;
- to encourage the use of estimation skills in deciding which number to key in to the calculator before halving it.
- to emphasise the inverse relationship of multiplication and division.

Previous mathematical knowledge and skill required

Awareness of the concept of division (sharing and grouping). Experience of the use of the constant functions for addition, subtraction and multiplication (see *Book 1* and earlier activities in this book).

Notes on using the page

This is a variation on the standard game of *Four in a line* or *Connect four*, but used here for a specific purpose. The game rules are self-explanatory, but it is wise to ensure that they are understood.
It is also important that the use of constants for addition, subtraction and multiplication have already been experienced, and that the additional activities are attempted. If a child has difficulty, show how each player is attempting to key in a number which is *double* one that is shown on the grid. Stress that the use of C or C/CE will remove the constant 'set up'; accidental clearing should be followed by a resetting of the function, as shown on the sheet.

●　●　●　●　●　●

Answers/Solutions

See above.

○ Ⓝ ⓪ Ⓣ Ⓔ Ⓢ

EQUIPMENT

 Calculator.

○
○ 25 *small* red counters and 25 *small* blue counters.

ADDITIONAL ACTIVITIES EXTENSIONS

1. Discuss the fact that halving can produce an odd number as an answer, whereas doubling (a whole number) always produces an even number.

2. Discuss reasons why 0 (zero) has been omitted from the grid.

3. Play the same game on a standard 100 square, or on a 10 by 10 multiplication square.

Join four today!

A game for 2 players.
One player has 25 red counters, the other has 25 blue counters.
Share **one** calculator.

Set the calculator for **divide by 2** like this: Press ②÷÷=⓪ .
Take turns.   Choose a number.
Key it into the calculator. Then press = .

If the display number is on this grid, and uncovered,
put a counter of **your** colour on it.
The first to get a line of four of his or her counters wins!

A line can be • • • •   or   ⋮   or   ⋱   or   ⋰

11	38	18	65	47	2	31
43	1	34	21	17	80	250
8	14	100	41	90	37	5
32	53	70	4	77	50	16
60	6	55	150	13	66	200
12	67	42	36	19	9	33
3	44	15	51	7	39	69

Name _____   Class _____

GAME USING THE CONSTANT FUNCTION FOR DIVISION BY 2 (HALVING).

© Unwin Hyman
Calculated to Please 2

Name that train 1 and 2 ⑭–⑮

● ● ● ● ● ●

Activity/Purpose

The activity, which is shown on the two pages overleaf, uses the calculator to complete and name a series of sequences of numbers generated by constant addition, subtraction, multiplication and division. The purpose is to reinforce the use of the constant function while encouraging estimation skills and the analysis of patterns in number.

Previous mathematical knowledge and skill required

Experience of setting up the calculator for constants and their use in games and activities. Experience of the concepts and methods of the four rules of number.

Notes on using the pages

Ensure that the child has experience of the constant function of the calculator. If necessary discuss the simple worked example on the first sheet overleaf. Note that the 'name' of the train is, in fact, a number operation, e.g. +5.

Encourage the child to use systematic methods, e.g. to look for two adjacent, or near, windows and estimate/calculate the size of the gap between them. Then to check the hypothesis for the rest of the series by moving towards the next available given number. Encourage the child to use the calculator to *check* ideas rather than relying too much upon its functions.

● ● ● ● ● ●

Answers/Solutions

1.	21	28	35	42	49	56	63	70	77	(+7)
2.	99	91	83	75	67	59	51	43	35	(−8)
3.	216	209	202	195	188	181	174	167	160	(−7)
4.	1	20	39	58	77	96	115	134	153	(+19)
5.	135	120	105	90	75	60	45	30	15	(−15)
6.	5	8	11	14	17	20	23	26	29	(+3)
7.	1	2	4	8	16	32	64	128	256	(×2)
8.	768	384	192	96	48	24	12	6	3	(÷2)
9.	106	93	80	67	54	41	28	15	2	(−13)

Ⓞ Ⓝ Ⓞ Ⓣ Ⓔ Ⓢ

EQUIPMENT

Calculator.

ADDITIONAL ACTIVITIES EXTENSIONS

1. Having established the pattern in any sequence, encourage the child to continue it in either direction. This will raise the problem of negative numbers, which can be discussed in a suitable way, e.g. 'below ground' numbers.

2. Make use of the unnumbered blank opposite to:
   (a) use different sequences of numbers according to the ability of the child;
   (b) name the trains and require the generation of suitable sequences;
   (c) allow the child to invent and name his or her own sequences.

Name that train

NUMBER PATTERNS USING THE CONSTANT FUNCTION.

© Unwin Hyman
Calculated to Please 2

Use the **constant function** on your calculator –
and your brain!
Name the train.
Fill in the missing numbers on the windows,
like this.

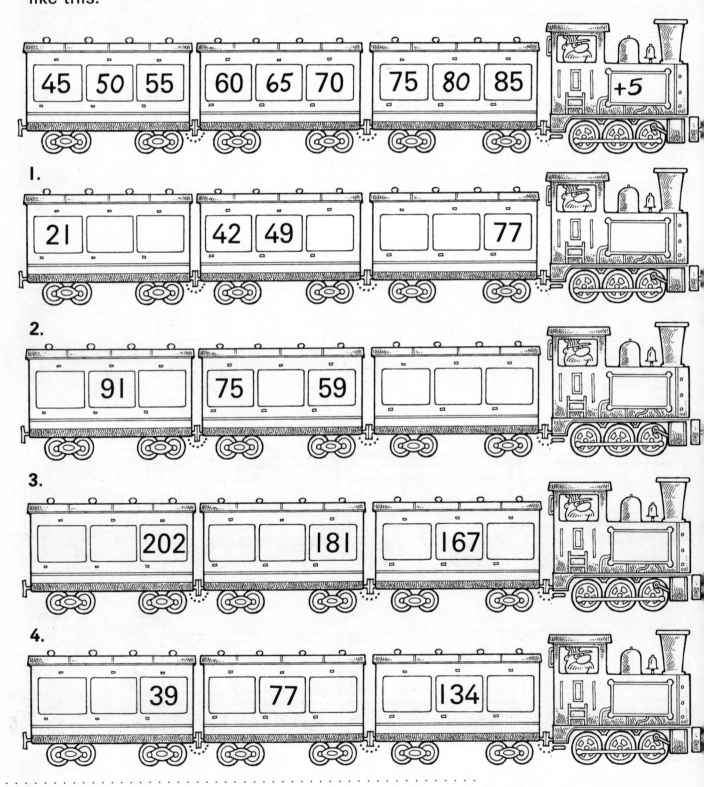

| 45 | 50 | 55 | 60 | 65 | 70 | 75 | 80 | 85 | +5 |

1.
| 21 | | | 42 | 49 | | | | 77 |

2.
| | 91 | | 75 | | 59 | | | |

3.
| | | 202 | | | 181 | | | 167 |

4.
| | | 39 | | | 77 | | | 134 |

Name _____

Class _____

NUMBER PATTERNS USING THE CONSTANT FUNCTION.

© Unwin Hyman
Calculated to Please 2

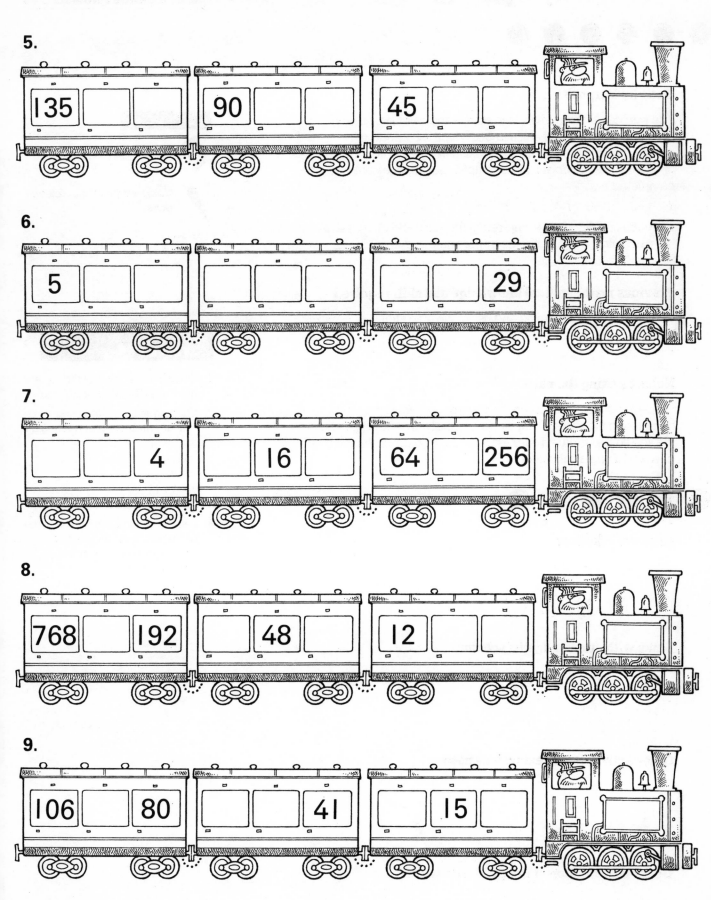

5. 135 | 90 | 45

6. 5 | | 29

7. 4 | 16 | 64 | 256

8. 768 | 192 | 48 | 12

9. 106 | 80 | 41 | 15

Name _____ Class _____

NUMBER PATTERNS USING THE CONSTANT FUNCTION.

© Unwin Hyman
Calculated to Please 2

Four-way split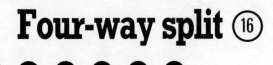

● ● ● ● ● ●

Activity/Purpose

The purpose of the activity is to encourage calculator use in
creating and checking calculations which use addition,
subtraction, multiplication and division in order to achieve a series
of given target numbers. For example, the first line could be
completed thus:

7 4+3   10−3   7×1   21÷3

For each correct answer entered in the grid (and checked using
the calculator) a quarter of the appropriate 'tile' is coloured.

Previous mathematical knowledge and skill required

Knowledge of the meaning and use of the operations +, −, ×, ÷.
Counting skills to at least 150.

Notes on using the page

There are no instructions on the page so explain the method of
completing the sheet. Point out, particularly, that the appropriate
tile should be coloured *after* a cell on the grid has been filled and
checked using a calculator.

● ● ● ● ● ●

Answers/Solutions

Open-ended (see above).

Links with our own maths scheme

Other activities and extensions used

General evaluation of the children's work

EQUIPMENT

 Calculator.

 Coloured pencils or felt-tip
pens.

ADDITIONAL ACTIVITIES
EXTENSIONS

1. Discuss the pattern of the target
numbers (the table of sevens).

2. Encourage the child to create
similar patterns in completing the
grid, e.g.:

  7=7+0
14=7+7
21=7+14
28=7+21   and so on.

3. Use the unnumbered sheet at the
back of the book to examine
other sequences, including
random entries.

Four way split

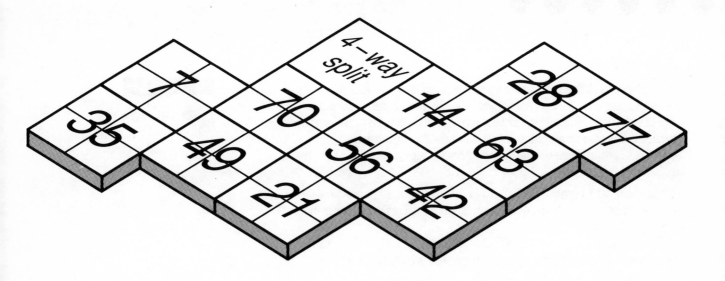

	+	−	✕	÷
7				
14				
21				
28				
35				
42				
49				
56				
63				
70				
77				

Name _____   Class _____

USING THE FOUR RULES OF NUMBER TO REACH TARGET NUMBERS.

© Unwin Hyman
Calculated to Please 2

Hot hundreds 1, 2 and 3 ⑰–⑲

Activity/Purpose

Competence in the manipulation of the numbers 1 to 100 is an essential aspect of everyday arithmetic. These pages encourage the child to work carefully and systematically, using a combination of mental, written and calculator-based methods, in order to complete sequences or number sentences which lead to or from 100.

Hot hundreds 1 requires the child to determine and record one, two or three 2-digit numbers which link a given starting number to 100 by addition.
Hot hundreds 2 requires the child to determine and record one, two or three single-digit or 2-digit numbers which link 100 to a given target number by subtraction.
Hot hundreds 3 is an activity in problem solving/investigation. The child chooses where to use ⊞ or ⊟ in a series of 'necklaces' to make the number sentences true. In each necklace the numbers are the digits 1, 2, 3, 4, 5, 6, 7, 8 and 9, used in order but in different combinations.

Previous mathematical knowledge and skill required

Experiences of addition and subtraction to 100 by counting on or back.

Notes on using the pages

Remind the child that all inputs should be *greater than 10*. Explain that when two inputs are required the chosen numbers should be different to each other. Allow a less able child to use multiples of 10 to get close to the target, but encourage a more able child to use less obvious numbers.
When using *Hot hundreds 3*, encourage the child to work in rough in pencil, trying out possibilities before finally writing the solution on the sheet.

Answers/Solutions

Hot hundreds 3

$1+2+3-4+5+6+78+9=100$
$12+3-4+5+67+8+9=100$
$123+45-67+8-9=100$
$123-45-67+89=100$
$12-3-4+5-6+7+89=100$
$1+23-4+5+6+78-9=100$
$1+23-4+56+7+8+9=100$

EQUIPMENT

 Calculator.

ADDITIONAL ACTIVITIES EXTENSIONS

Use the unnumbered blanks supplied at the back of the book to examine other numbers of your own or the child's choice. The sheets are easily edited, so encourage less able children to examine targets lower than 100, and more able children to examine targets of 1000 or more.

Hot hundreds 1

⑰ ●●●●●●●

Use only numbers larger than 10.

Key in **one number** to change each starter to 100.

28.	+		= 100
71.	+		= 100
57.	+		= 100
13.	+		= 100

Key in **two different numbers** to change each starter to 100.

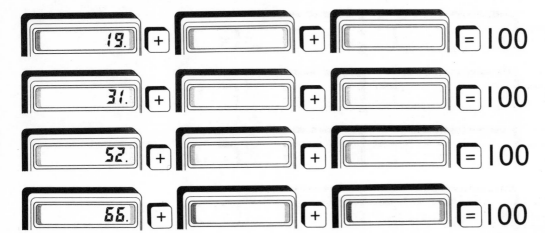

19.	+		+		= 100
31.	+		+		= 100
52.	+		+		= 100
66.	+		+		= 100

Key in **three different numbers** to change each starter to 100.

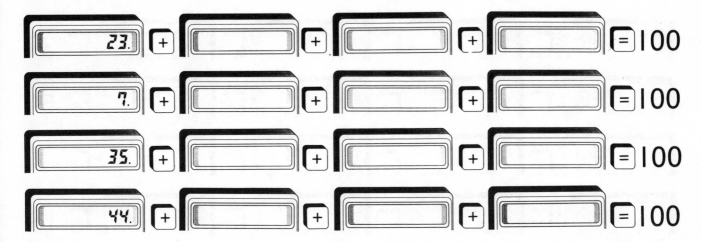

23.	+		+		+		= 100
7.	+		+		+		= 100
35.	+		+		+		= 100
44.	+		+		+		= 100

Name _____   Class _____

ESTIMATING AND CHECKING ADDITION OF NUMBERS TO 100.

© Unwin Hyman
Calculated to Please 2

Hot hundreds 2

⑱ ● ● ● ● ● ●

Use only numbers larger than 10.

Start with 100. Key in **one number** to change it to the target.

100. − ☐ = 77

100. − ☐ = 59

100. − ☐ = 33

100. − ☐ = 14

Start with 100. Key in **two numbers** to change it to the target.

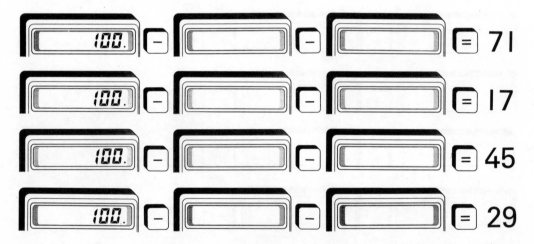

100. − ☐ − ☐ = 71

100. − ☐ − ☐ = 17

100. − ☐ − ☐ = 45

100. − ☐ − ☐ = 29

Start with 100. Key in **three numbers** to change it to the target.

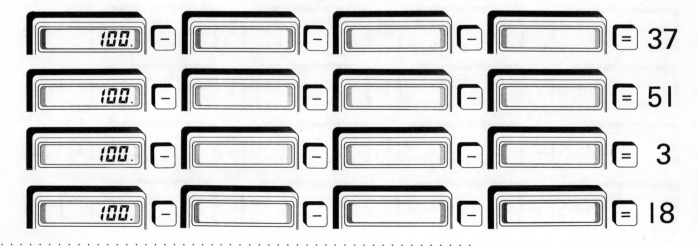

100. − ☐ − ☐ − ☐ = 37

100. − ☐ − ☐ − ☐ = 51

100. − ☐ − ☐ − ☐ = 3

100. − ☐ − ☐ − ☐ = 18

Name _____   Class _____

ESTIMATING AND CHECKING SUBTRACTION OF NUMBERS FROM 100.

© Unwin Hyman
Calculated to Please 2

Hot hundreds 3

 ⑲

Choose ⊞ or ⊟ for the blank keys to make each necklace total 100.

100

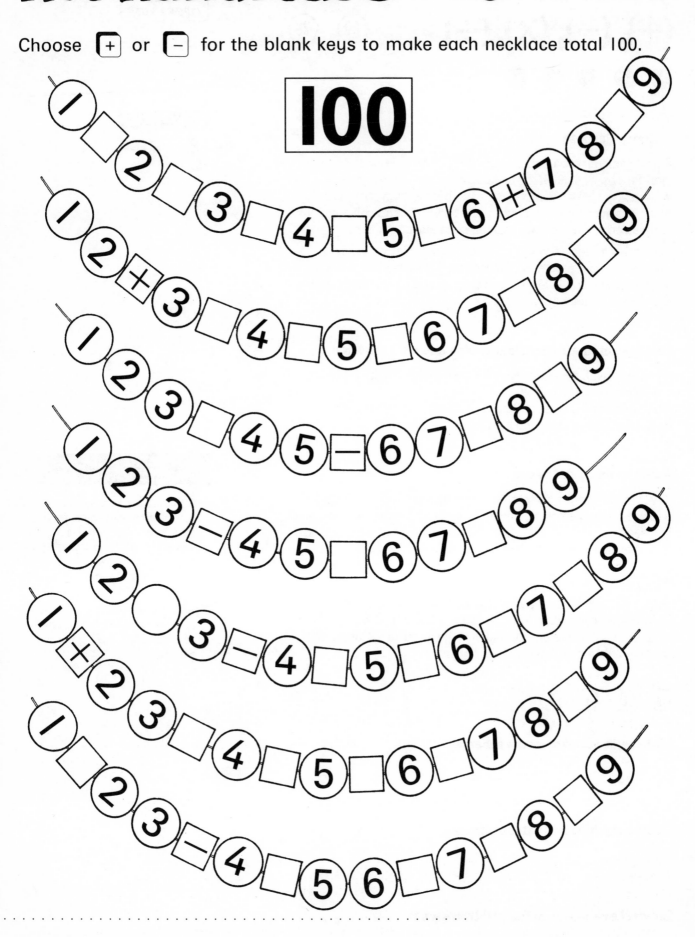

Name _____ Class _____

PROBLEM SOLVING AND INVESTIGATION USING ADDITION AND SUBTRACTION.

© Unwin Hyman
Calculated to Please 2

Words for numbers
$(+), (-), (\times), (\div)$

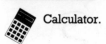

Activity/Purpose

A large amount of calculator work is dealt with orally. It is therefore essential that the child develops the ability to:
- interpret spoken numbers and numbers written out in full;
- understand all the vocabulary used officially and colloquially to mean addition, subtraction, multiplication and division.

The ability to decide which operation to use in a particular situation is reinforced and practised on the following four pages, along with the ability to read and translate numbers into figures and/or combinations of numerals.

Previous mathematical knowledge and skill required

Familiarity with the concepts of addition, subtraction, multiplication and division.
Familiarity with the use of a calculator to compute when the figures and symbols for the operations are given.

Notes on using the pages

Deal with the pages one at a time, making sure that each can be done correctly before moving on to the next. Ensure that the child can 'read', i.e. decode the words used, before briefly discussing the different ways in which each operation can be stated. The child then works through the page, ringing the digital answers which match those he or she obtains.

Follow through with further teaching of the forms of wording which cause difficulties. The use of the calculator allows concentration on the interpretation of the terms used rather than on the number manipulation.

EQUIPMENT

Calculator.

ADDITIONAL ACTIVITIES EXTENSIONS

1. Compare and contrast the terms used as part of the different operations; e.g. 'from' (in addition and subtraction); 'together' and 'total' (in addition and multiplication); 'times' (in multiplication and division).

2. Encourage calculator use in the checking of 'word problems' in your mainstream mathematics scheme.

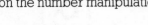 ○ Ⓝ Ⓞ Ⓣ Ⓔ Ⓢ

Links with our own maths scheme

Other activities and extensions used

General evaluation of the children's work

Words for numbers (+) ㉠

When we 'say' a number we use words.

There are many ways to tell you to **add**.

All the ways used on this page want you to **add** numbers.

Use your calculator to do these additions.
Each time, check **your** answer with the answer on the page.
If the answers match, your answer is right
and you can ring the answer on the page.

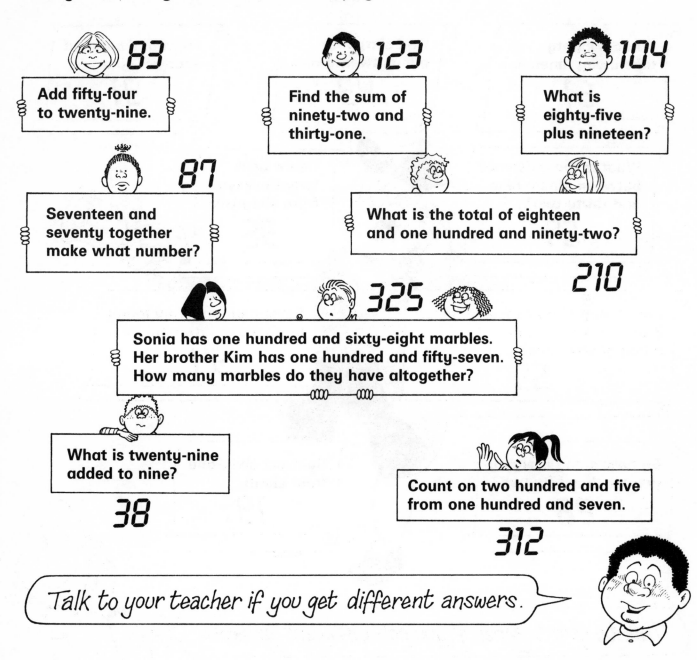

83

**Add fifty-four
to twenty-nine.**

123

**Find the sum of
ninety-two and
thirty-one.**

104

**What is
eighty-five
plus nineteen?**

87

**Seventeen and
seventy together
make what number?**

**What is the total of eighteen
and one hundred and ninety-two?**

210

325

**Sonia has one hundred and sixty-eight marbles.
Her brother Kim has one hundred and fifty-seven.
How many marbles do they have altogether?**

**What is twenty-nine
added to nine?**

38

**Count on two hundred and five
from one hundred and seven.**

312

Talk to your teacher if you get different answers.

Name _____ Class _____

USING A CALCULATOR FOR ADDITION CALCULATIONS PRESENTED IN WORD
FORM. REVISION AND EXTENSION OF ALTERNATIVE FORMS OF 'ADD'.

© Unwin Hyman
Calculated to Please 2

When we 'say' a number we use words.

There are many ways to tell you to **subtract**.

All the ways used on this page want you to **subtract** numbers.

Use your calculator to do these subtractions.
Each time, check **your** answer with the answer on the page.
If the answers match, your answer is right
and you can ring the answer on the page.

What is eighty take away nineteen?

61

Find sixty-four minus twenty-one.

43

From one hundred subtract nine.

91

What is the difference between ninety-nine and thirty-two?

67

Count back twenty-seven from sixty-two.

35

How many marbles would be left if you took six out of a bag of sixty-one?

55

Seventeen and how many more make fifty-one?

34

By how many is eighty greater than fifty-two?

28

Subtract sixty-one from eighty.

19

Talk to your teacher if you get different answers.

Name _____ Class _____

USING A CALCULATOR FOR SUBTRACTION CALCULATIONS PRESENTED IN
WORD FORM. REVISION AND EXTENSION OF ALTERNATIVE FORMS OF
'SUBTRACT'.

© Unwin Hyman
Calculated to Please 2

When we 'say' a number we use words.

There are many ways to tell you to **multiply**.

All the ways used on this page want you to **multiply** numbers.

Use your calculator to do these multiplications.
Each time, check **your** answer with the answer on the page.
If the answers match, your answer is right
and you can ring the answer on the page.

Multiply seventeen by seventy.

1190

What is sixty-two multiplied by twenty-one?

1302

How many altogether in eleven sets of one hundred and one?

1111

What are thirty-one sixes?

186

How many is two hundred and three times twenty-seven?

5481

Seven packets of sweets each have twenty-two in them. What is the total number of sweets?

154

What is the product of ninety-nine and one hundred and five?

10395

Talk to your teacher if you get different answers.

Name _____ Class _____

USING A CALCULATOR FOR MULTIPLICATION CALCULATIONS PRESENTED IN
WORD FORM. REVISION AND EXTENSION OF ALTERNATIVE FORMS OF
'MULTIPLY'.

© Unwin Hyman
Calculated to Please 2

Words for numbers (÷)

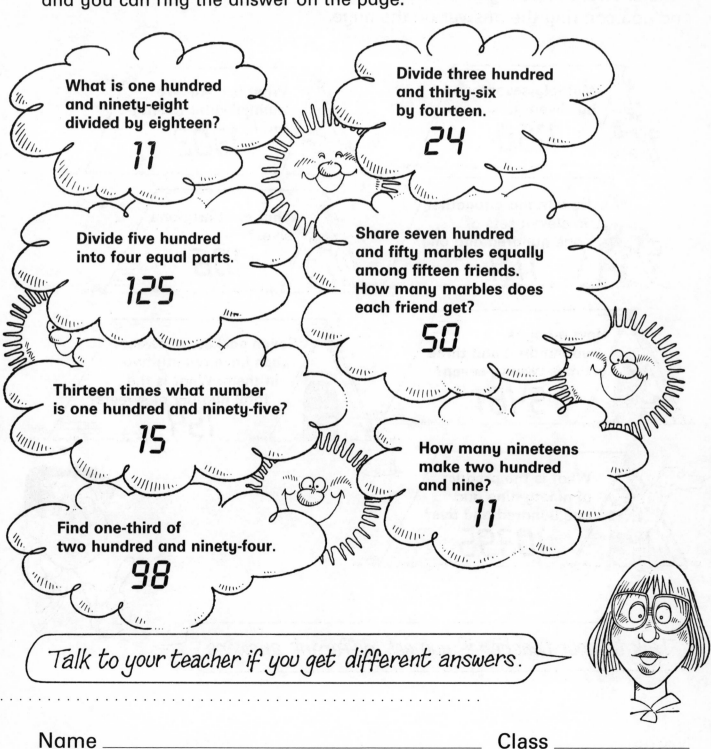

When we 'say' a number we use words.

There are many ways to tell you to **divide**.

All the ways used on this page want you to **divide** numbers.

Use your calculator to do these divisions.
Each time, check **your** answer with the answer on the page.
If the answers match, your answer is right
and you can ring the answer on the page.

What is one hundred and ninety-eight divided by eighteen?

11

Divide three hundred and thirty-six by fourteen.

24

Divide five hundred into four equal parts.

125

Share seven hundred and fifty marbles equally among fifteen friends. How many marbles does each friend get?

50

Thirteen times what number is one hundred and ninety-five?

15

How many nineteens make two hundred and nine?

11

Find one-third of two hundred and ninety-four.

98

Talk to your teacher if you get different answers.

Name _____ Class _____

USING A CALCULATOR FOR DIVISION CALCULATIONS OF WHOLE NUMBERS PRESENTED IN WORD FORM. REVISION AND EXTENSION OF ALTERNATIVE FORMS OF 'DIVIDE'.

© Unwin Hyman
Calculated to Please 2

Add the difference 1 and 2

● ● ● ● ●   ㉔ – ㉕

Activity/Purpose

The calculator is used on these pages to reduce the computational burden on a simple investigation which requires addition and subtraction of groups of numbers.

Given a series of regular shapes, the child calculates the difference between the numbers on adjacent vertices. Working clockwise, if the first number is *larger* than the second number the answer is written *outside* the shape; if the first number is *smaller* than the second number the answer is written *inside* the shape. The two sets of answers are summed and found to be equal. The child completes the 'rule' on the second sheet and attempts brief explanations of why the rule works for different numbers and shapes.

Previous mathematical knowledge and skill required

Understanding of the terms *clockwise* and *difference*.
Ability to add and subtract using a calculator.

Notes on using the pages

Explain the rules of the activity using the worked example. Allow the child to attempt the triangle and pentagon unaided. Check that the technique is being used correctly before moving on to the more open-ended second page. Encourage the child to attempt the sentence completions on the second sheet without help.

● ● ● ● ●

Answers/Solutions

Triangle: 26+12   outside – total 38
             38   inside   – total 38

Pentagon: 12+98+36 outside – total 146
             83+63   inside – total 146

The inside and outside totals are equal.

Equal amounts cancel each other out.
Consider the worked example:
  inside ~~60~~–24+~~70~~–~~60~~+73–~~70~~=73–24=49
  outside 73–24=49
This could be shown algebraically but such abstraction is unnecessary.

EQUIPMENT

Calculator.

ADDITIONAL ACTIVITIES EXTENSIONS

These will follow from the child's attempts to explain the reason for the results. Other regular and non-regular polygons can be used, or the ones shown can be used with different numbers.

Ⓝ Ⓞ Ⓣ Ⓔ Ⓢ

Add the difference 1 ㉔

● ● ● ● ● ●

Work **clockwise** ↻ around each of these number shapes.

The first shape is done for you.
Talk to your teacher if you are not sure how to do them.

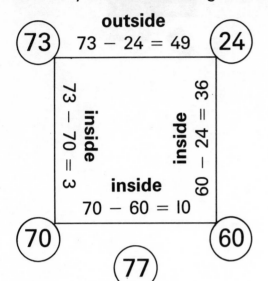

outside
73 − 24 = 49

inside
73 − 70 = 3

inside
60 − 24 = 36

inside
70 − 60 = 10

73 24

70 60

Answers
inside the shape

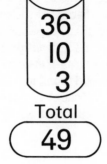

36
10
3

Total
49

Answers
outside the shape

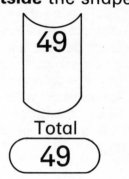

49

Total
49

77

39   51

Answers
inside the shape

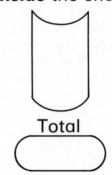

Total

Answers
outside the shape

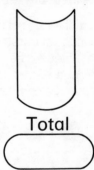

Total

29   17

65   100

2

Answers
inside the shape

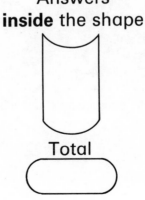

Total

Answers
outside the shape

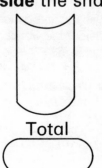

Total

Name _____

Class _____

NUMBER INVESTIGATION.

© Unwin Hyman
Calculated to Please 2

Add the difference 2 ㉕ ●●●●●●●

You choose the numbers around these shapes.

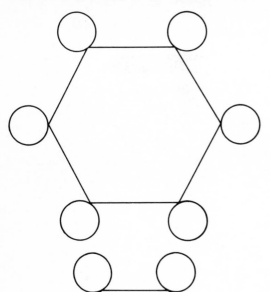

Answers **inside** the shape

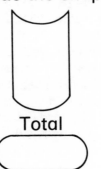

Total

Answers **outside** the shape

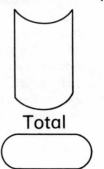

Total

Answers **inside** the shape

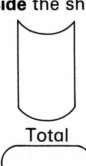

Total

Answers **outside** the shape

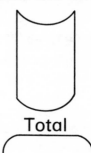

Total

The total of the answers inside each shape is equal to the total of

_____

I think this works for any number because _____

_____

_____

_____

I think this works for any shape because _____

_____

_____

_____

Name _____   Class _____

NUMBER INVESTIGATION.

© Unwin Hyman
Calculated to Please 2

Good guess 1 and 2 ㉖ – ㉗

Activity/Purpose

The ability to estimate the likely answer to a computation is a
fundamental skill of arithmetic. Practice at rounding and
approximation is encouraged by the use of a calculator, which
allows rapid checking and therefore an increased ability to
decide whether an answer is 'about right'. These pages require
the child to choose (from a given selection) a 'near' answer to each
computation. The calculator is then used to find the true answer,
which is compared with the estimate. The child is encouraged to
evaluate the quality of his or her estimates by deciding whether
the estimate is a 'good' guess or not.

Previous mathematical knowledge and skill required

Experience of the four rules of number in hundreds, tens and
units.

Notes on using the pages

Ensure that the child understands that the estimates must be made
before using the calculator.
Some children may need help with the technique of rounding
numbers in order to make the approximation easier, e.g. rounding
to the nearest 10. Encourage the child to work through the whole
set before evaluating the quality of the estimates. Discuss with the
child the techniques used and the ways in which he or she has
decided that an estimate was good or bad.

Answers/Solutions

In each case the best estimate is shown in brackets after the
calculation.

Sheet 1			Sheet 2		
47+22=	69	(70)	4×13=	52	(50)
51−19=	32	(30)	52÷ 5=	10·4	(10)
75+33=	108	(110)	78÷ 3=	26	(30)
90−18=	72	(70)	23× 4=	92	(90)
43+49=	92	(90)	6×17=	102	(100)
34+58=	92	(90)	19× 3=	57	(60)
74−46=	28	(30)	100÷ 3=	33·33	(30)
81−49=	32	(30)	37× 3=	111	(110)
83−25=	58	(60)	77÷ 5=	15·4	(20)
95+36=	131	(130)	82÷ 4=	20·5	(20)

EQUIPMENT

 Calculator.

ADDITIONAL ACTIVITIES EXTENSIONS

1. An unnumbered blank of the
   page is supplied overleaf for
   further practice using
   calculations of your choice and
   estimates at whatever degree of
   accuracy is required. For
   example, numbers in the
   hundreds can be used or the
   intervals between the given
   estimates can be reduced to 5.

2. Encourage investigation of what
   makes some of the best estimates
   higher than the true answer and
   others lower than the true
   answer.

Ⓝ Ⓞ Ⓣ Ⓔ Ⓢ

Good guess 1

Often we need to make a **good guess** at an answer.
A good guess is called an **estimate**.

For each question, ring the **estimate** you think is closest
to the true answer.
When you have done them all, check them using your calculator.

Question	Estimates				True answer	Good guess? Bad guess?
47 + 22	60	70	80	90		
51 − 19	30	40	50	60		
75 + 33	80	90	100	110		
90 − 18	60	70	80	90		
43 + 49	80	90	100	110		
34 + 58	70	80	90	100		
74 − 46	20	30	40	50		
81 − 49	30	40	50	60		
83 − 25	50	60	70	80		
95 + 36	110	120	130	140		

Name _____ Class _____

ESTIMATION AND CALCULATOR CHECKING IN ADDITION AND SUBTRACTION.

© Unwin Hyman
Calculated to Please 2

Good guess 2

● ● ● ● ● ●

Often we need to make a **good guess** at an answer.
A good guess is called an **estimate**.

For each question, ring the **estimate** you think is closest
to the true answer.
When you have done them all, check them using your calculator.

Question	Estimates				True answer	Good guess? Bad guess?
4 × 13	40	50	60	70		
52 ÷ 5	10	20	30	40		
78 ÷ 3	10	20	30	40		
23 × 4	80	90	100	110		
6 × 17	80	90	100	110		
19 × 3	40	50	60	70		
100 ÷ 3	20	30	40	50		
37 × 3	90	100	110	120		
77 ÷ 5	10	20	30	40		
82 ÷ 4	10	20	30	40		

Name _____ Class _____

ESTIMATION AND CALCULATOR CHECKING IN MULTIPLICATION AND DIVISION.

© Unwin Hyman
Calculated to Please 2

Good guess

Often we need to make a **good guess** at an answer.
A good guess is called an **estimate**.

For each question, ring the **estimate** you think is closest
to the true answer.
When you have done them all, check them using your calculator.

Question	Estimates	True answer	Good guess? Bad guess?

Name _____ Class _____

ESTIMATION AND CALCULATOR CHECKING IN ADDITION AND SUBTRACTION. © Unwin Hyman
Calculated to Please 2

Calc-busters ㉘

● ● ● ● ● ●

Activity/Purpose

The activity is a game for two players. The aim of each player is to get a line of counters across the board in his or her colour, either blue or green. Note that a winning line across the grid can twist and turn and need not proceed in a straight line; however it should begin at the appropriate 'Start' line and end at the appropriate 'Finish' line.

Previous mathematical knowledge and skill required

Awareness and facility with the concepts and operations of multiplication and division.

Notes on using the page

The players take turns to choose either one or two of the numbers in this list.

| 5 | 6 | 7 | 8 | 9 | 10 | 11 | 12 |

It would be helpful to write them on a small card for the players to refer to when playing. Each player states aloud his or her chosen number(s). Using a calculator (whether or not the answer is known) the single number is multiplied by itself (squared) *or* the two numbers are multiplied to find the product.
If the answer is on the board the player can place a counter of his or her colour on it. If the space is occupied, another containing the same number can be used. If there is no numbered space for that answer, the child misses that turn.

EQUIPMENT

One calculator, shared.

Blue and green counters.

ADDITIONAL ACTIVITIES EXTENSIONS

1. An unnumbered sheet of *Calc-busters* is supplied at the back of the book for you to develop the game to larger numbers and encourage the children to design their own game.

2. Encourage discussion of patterns in the relevant 'tables' used in the game.

3. Develop the game so that *two* square numbers must be included in the winning line.

◯ Ⓝ ◯ Ⓣ Ⓔ Ⓢ

Links with our own maths scheme

Other activities and extensions used

General evaluation of the children's work

CALC BUSTERS

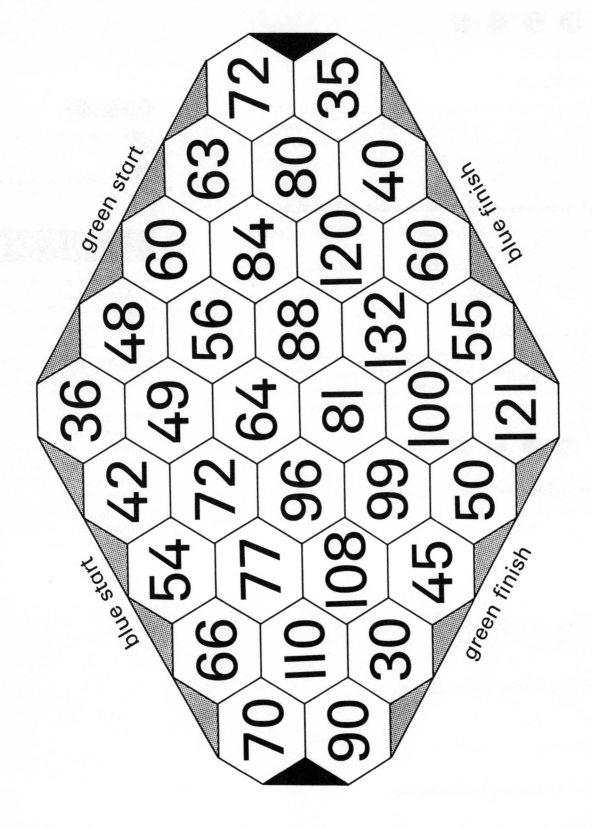

Blue name _____

Green name _____

Class _____

A GAME OF STRATEGY, USING MULTIPLICATION BONDS TO 132,
REINFORCED BY CALCULATOR USE.

© Unwin Hyman
Calculated to Please 2

Gobbler!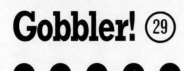

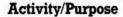

Activity/Purpose

The purpose of the activity is to encourage the child to estimate likely totals produced by the addition of numbers, and then to check them using a calculator. The child finds a route for *Gobbler* to the edge of the grid, which produces the given target number.

Previous mathematical knowledge and skill required

Experience of the concept and process of addition of numbers in hundreds, tens and units.
Familiarity with the rounding technique for estimation of sums of numbers.

Notes on using the page

Ensure that the child has the necessary pre-requisite knowledge. Reinforce the instruction to change direction only *once* after leaving the starting box. The route can be defined using a coloured line, or the set of boxes can be fully coloured.

Answers/Solutions

The route to 151 sweets is $11+17+69+48+6$

EQUIPMENT

 Calculator.

 Coloured pencil or felt-tip pen.

ADDITIONAL ACTIVITIES EXTENSIONS

Use the unnumbered blank of the sheet, at the back of the book, for further related activities, such as:

1. Using much smaller numbers (<10) for less able children.

2. Using 'round' numbers.

3. Using odd (or even) numbers only.

4. Finding the maximum/minimum number of sweets that can be eaten.

5. Allowing two or more changes of direction after leaving the starting point.

6. Allowing a given number of moves, e.g. 2, 3, 4 and so on, to achieve the maximum number.

7. Allowing the child to try his or her own choice of target numbers.

    N O T E S

Links with our own maths scheme

Other activities and extensions used

General evaluation of the children's work

Gobbler !

Gobbler is a sweet eater!
She always starts in the middle and
goes to an edge.
She can only move **up** ↑ or **down** ↓
or **right** → or **left** ←

The numbers show how many sweets
in each box.
Gobbler can only change direction **once**
after starting.
Colour Gobbler's journey to eat 151 sweets.

44	6	21	77	8	36	10
2	66	12	40	15	2	11
61	13	41	3	55	33	79
5	32	4	START HERE	11	17	7
71	17	19	5	91	69	51
88	16	59	14	20	48	18
1	15	26	37	29	6	9

At the end Gobbler was sick!

Name _____

Class _____

ESTIMATION AND PROBLEM SOLVING.

© Unwin Hyman
Calculated to Please 2

Octo-plus!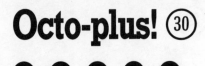

Activity/Purpose

The activity is a puzzle-format 'problem' requiring the child to choose routes through a grid (4 by 4) in order to achieve specified target numbers. The routes are marked using different coloured pencils or felt-tips.

Previous mathematical knowledge and skill required

Experience of the four rules of number.

Notes on using the page

Reinforce the child's awareness that the grid requires movement from bottom left to top right, using the arrows to show direction in a vertical, or horizontal direction. Diagonal moves, and movements to the left or downwards, are not allowed.

Answers/Solutions

Route to 100 is $0 + 7 \times 6 - 17 \div 5 \times 20$

Route to 200 is $0 + 8 \times 4 \div 2 - 6 \times 20$

Route to 19 is $0 + 8 \times 4 + 23 \div 5 + 8$

EQUIPMENT

Calculator.

 Red, yellow and green coloured pencils or crayons or felt-tip pens.

ADDITIONAL ACTIVITIES EXTENSIONS

Make an unnumbered blank of the page. This can be used to investigate other sets of numbers and operations of your choice, or the child's choice. Possible extensions are:

1. Use of only *one* operation: +, −, ×, or ÷.

2. Use of numbers which are with a particular 'table', e.g. the table of threes or fives.

3. Use of two operations, specified or free choice.

4. Use of numbers which are always less than, or greater than, a given figure.

     N O T E S

Links with our own maths scheme

Other activities and extensions used

General evaluation of the children's work

Octo-plus !

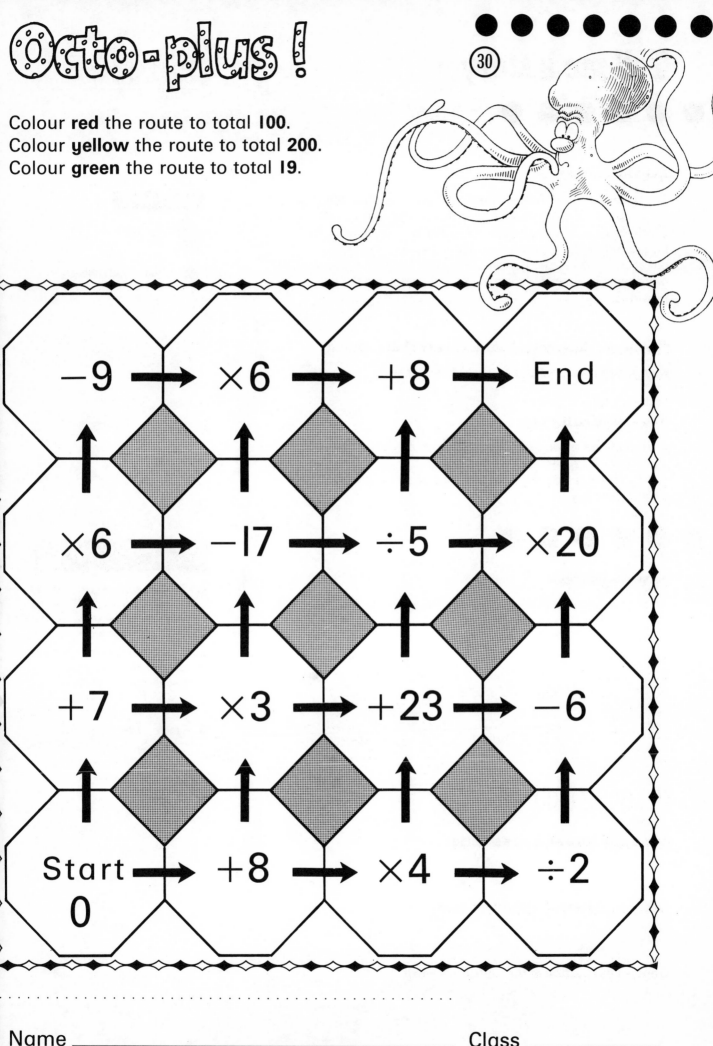

Colour **red** the route to total **100**.
Colour **yellow** the route to total **200**.
Colour **green** the route to total **19**.

㉚

−9 →	×6 →	+8 →	End
↑	↑	↑	↑
×6 →	−17 →	÷5 →	×20
↑	↑	↑	↑
+7 →	×3 →	+23 →	−6
↑	↑	↑	↑
Start 0 →	+8 →	×4 →	÷2

Name _____

Class _____

USING THE FOUR RULES TO ACHIEVE TARGET NUMBERS (PUZZLE).

© Unwin Hyman
Calculated to Please 2

Tell me a story ㉛

Activity/Purpose

The purpose is to encourage keyboard fluency by the completion of a simple story with upside-down calculator-display 'words'. Practice in the concept of place value and the four rules is included. The child presses the keys in the correct order to complete a calculation. The calculator is then inverted to read the 'word', which is then written in normal handwriting in the box provided.

Previous mathematical knowledge and skill required

Knowledge of the meaning and use of the signs +, −, ×, ÷.

Notes on using the page

First show one or two examples of how to 'read' the display,
e.g.   leg ⟷ *LE9* ⟷ inverted 637.
The activity is self-checking, since an incorrect input will produce a useless display.

Answers/Solutions

After each calculation, the word can be found by 'reading' the digital number in the display upside down.
The words used in the story are as follows:

Bob	808	She	345	Goes	5306
Elsie	31573	Leg	637	Oh	40
Bill	7718	Goggles	5376606	Oozes	53200
Hill	7714	Oil	710	Shoe	3045
Sell	7735	Bib	818	Giggle	376616
I	1	Billie	317718	Boohoo	0·04008
Lis(t)	517				

EQUIPMENT

Calculator.

Pencil and rubber.

ADDITIONAL ACTIVITIES EXTENSIONS

1. Children can begin producing their own words, sentences and stories using the words produced on the page as the base.

2. Children can begin systematic listing of the possible words. Note that none can use A, C, D, F, J, K, M, N, P, Q, R, T, U, V, W, X, Y.

3. A more systematic activity to analyse the possible words can be found in *Book 3*.

Ⓝ Ⓞ Ⓣ Ⓔ Ⓢ

Links with our own maths scheme

Other activities and extensions used

General evaluation of the children's work

Tell me a story

One day 202 × 4 [＿＿＿] and 31500 + 73 [＿＿＿] go

shopping. They go to the shop owned by 3859 × 2 [＿＿＿] .

The shop is on a 9848 − 2134 [＿＿＿] .

"Will you 15 470 ÷ 2 [＿＿＿] me these things?" says

31 474 + 99 [＿＿＿] . "56 ÷ 56 [＿.＿] have brought a

450 + 67 [＿＿＿] t."

69 × 5 [＿＿＿] reads the paper in her hand.

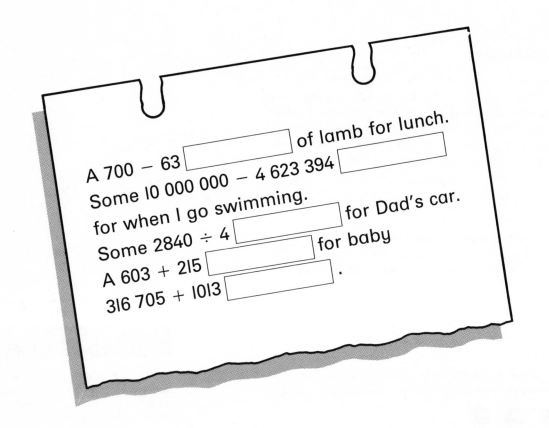

A 700 − 63 [＿＿＿] of lamb for lunch.

Some 10 000 000 − 4 623 394 [＿＿＿]

for when I go swimming.

Some 2840 ÷ 4 [＿＿＿] for Dad's car.

A 603 + 215 [＿＿＿] for baby

316 705 + 1013 [＿＿＿] .

23 154 ÷ 3 [＿＿＿] 5295 + 11 [＿＿＿] to get the things.

"Thank you," say the children. As they leave the shop

101 × 2 × 4 [＿＿＿] drops the bag. "120 ÷ 3 [＿＿＿] look!"

says the girl, "Things have broken." The 64 + 801 − 155 [＿＿＿]

665 × 80 [＿＿＿] out on to the boy's 719 × 5 − 550 [＿＿＿] .

The girl begins to 94 154 × 4 [＿＿＿] .

"240 480 ÷ 6 000 000 [＿＿＿] ," cries the boy.

Name ＿＿＿＿＿＿＿＿＿＿＿＿＿＿＿＿＿ Class ＿＿＿＿＿＿＿

UPSIDE-DOWN 'WORDS' ON A CALCULATOR.

© Unwin Hyman
Calculated to Please 2

Starting grids 1 and 2

Activity/Purpose

The purpose of the activity is to complete or create a two-dimensional grid of numbers derived from constant addition or subtraction. Once completed, the grid can be used to examine number patterns and sequences.

Previous mathematical knowledge and skill required

Experience with the constant functions for addition and subtraction.

Notes on using the pages

Discuss with the child the fact that the grids can be completed in a number of ways, using the constant functions. For example, using one constant to create the first row or column and then the other constant to complete the grid; alternatively a combination can be used on a continual basis to build the grid from the top left to the bottom right. Some of the numbers have been included on each grid to provide checks as the sequences are written.

Discuss the patterns which emerge and are written out by the child, e.g.:

Starting grid 1: diagonals are counting numbers.
diagonals increase by 15 (8+7).
digit sum of top line is the sequence 1, 9, 8, 7, 6, 5, 4, 3, 2, 1.

Starting grid 2: digit sum of first column is 1 for each cell.
diagonals increase by 3 (9−6).
diagonals decrease by 15 (9+6).

There are many others.

The subtraction sheet will produce negative numbers. Use them or ignore them, depending on the ability of the child.

EQUIPMENT

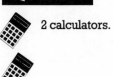 2 calculators.

ADDITIONAL ACTIVITIES EXTENSIONS

Use the unnumbered blank of the sheet (overleaf) to examine other starting numbers, or, for example, addition horizontally on the grid and subtraction vertically.

Answers/Solutions

+8

10	18	26	34	42	50	58	66	74	82
17	25	33	41	49	57	65	73	81	89
24	32	40	48	56	64	72	80	88	96
31	39	47	55	63	71	79	87	95	103
38	46	54	62	70	78	86	94	102	110
45	53	61	69	77	85	93	101	109	117
52	60	68	76	84	92	100	108	116	124
59	67	75	83	91	99	107	115	123	131
66	74	82	90	98	106	114	122	130	138
73	81	89	97	105	113	121	129	137	145

+7

−6

100	94	88	82	76	70	64	58	52	46
91	85	79	73	67	61	55	49	43	37
82	76	70	64	58	52	46	40	34	28
73	67	61	55	49	43	37	31	25	19
64	58	52	46	40	34	28	22	16	10
55	49	43	37	31	25	19	13	7	1
46	40	34	28	22	16	10	4	−2	−8
37	31	25	19	13	7	1	−5	−11	−17
28	22	16	10	4	−2	−8	−14	−20	−26
19	13	7	1	−5	−11	−17	−23	−29	−35

−9

Fill in the missing numbers on this grid.

Use 2 calculators.

Set one for **add 8** like this 8 $+$ $+$ $=$ 0

Set the other for **add** 7 like this 7 $+$ $+$ $=$ 0

+8 →

START •

+7 ↓

10	18	26							
17	25						73		
24									
								95	
						85			
							115		
		82							

Find some patterns in the numbers which go
across the grid,   up and down   and on a slope. ↖

⇔   ⇕   ↙ ↘

Write about them on the back of this sheet.

Name _____   Class _____

CREATING AND ANALYSING NUMBER PATTERNS OF CONSTANT ADDITION.

© Unwin Hyman
Calculated to Please 2

Starting grids 2

● ● ● ● ● ●

Fill in the missing numbers on this grid.
Go as far as you can.

Use 2 calculators.

Set one for **subtract 6** like this ⑥ ⊟ ⊟ ⊟ ⓪

Set the other for **subtract 9** like this ⑨ ⊟ ⊟ ⊟ ⓪

→ **−6** →

START ●

−9

100	94	88							
91	85								
82									
						31			
					31			7	

Find some patterns in the numbers which go
across the grid,   up and down   and on a slope.

←→   ⇕   ↘

Write about them on the back of this sheet.

Name _____ Class _____

CREATING AND ANALYSING NUMBER PATTERNS OF CONSTANT SUBTRACTION.

© Unwin Hyman
Calculated to Please 2

Starting grids

Fill in the missing numbers on this grid.
Go as far as you can.

Use 2 calculators.

Set one for [   ] like this ⬜⬜⬜ = ⓪

Set the other for [   ] like this ⬜⬜⬜ = ⓪

START

Find some patterns in the numbers which go
across the grid,   up and down   and on a slope.

Write about them on the back of this sheet.

Name _____   Class _____

CREATING AND ANALYSING NUMBER PATTERNS OF CONSTANT SUBTRACTION.   © Unwin Hyman
Calculated to Please 2

Square magic 1, 2 and 3 ㉞–㊱

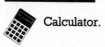

Activity/Purpose

The activity involves investigation of magic squares, using a calculator for addition and subtraction. It includes the transformation of magic squares by constants of the four rules of number, and the use of numbers larger than those normally convenient for mental or written methods.

Previous mathematical knowledge and skill required

Experience of the concepts and techniques of the four rules of number.
Familiarity with the means of setting a constant into the calculator and using it to convert sets of numbers.

Notes on using the pages

Deal with the pages separately, but in the given sequence. Ensure that the basic idea of a magic square is understood.
Encourage the child to use the calculator when necessary, but not for every calculation, since some are quicker and easier to deal with mentally.
Ensure that the child calculates and records the 'magic number' of each square; it is these which form the basis of the principles which emerge on sheets 2 and 3 of the set.

EQUIPMENT

Calculator.

ADDITIONAL ACTIVITIES EXTENSIONS

1. Discuss the method used by the child to complete the magic squares, to assess the degree of consistency and the extent to which the child works systematically.

2. Encourage the child to seek out and check magic squares found in mainstream schemes and other supplementary mathematics materials.

3. Discuss the relationships which have emerged between the linked magic numbers on the second and third sheets, i.e.:

   B *Add 37* Adding 37 to each number increases the first magic number by 3×37=111.

   C *Subtract 27* Subtracting 27 from each number decreases the first magic number by 3×27=81.

   D *Multiply by 7* Multiplying each number by 7 increases the first magic number sevenfold.

   E *Divide by 8* Dividing each number by 8 divides the first magic number by 8.

   F Addition of two magic squares produces a new magic square, the magic number of which is the sum of the first two.

   G Subtraction of one magic square from another produces a new magic square, the magic number of which is the difference between the first two.

Answers/Solutions

A 1.

4	3	8
9	5	1
2	7	6

(15)

2.

15	20	13
14	16	18
19	12	17

(48)

3.

47	54	49
52	50	48
51	46	53

(150)

4.

16	3	2	13
5	10	11	8
9	6	7	12
4	15	14	1

(34)

5.

23	13	12	26
18	20	21	15
22	16	17	19
11	25	24	14

(74)

6.

19	61	88	96
98	86	69	11
66	18	91	89
81	99	16	68

(264)

B

50	55	48
49	51	53
54	47	52

(153)

C

44	39	40
37	41	45
42	43	38

(123)

D

98	63	70
49	77	105
84	91	56

(231)

E

11	18	13
16	14	12
15	10	17

(42)

F

60	72	60
64	64	64
68	56	68

(192)

G

58	71	63
69	64	59
65	57	70

(192)

Square magic 1

A magic square

Magic number

18

7	8	3
2	6	10
9	4	5

→ 7 + 8 + 3 = 18

→ 2 + 6 + 10 = 18

→ 9 + 4 + 5 = 18

7 + 6 + 5 = 18

7   8   3
+   +   +
2   6   10
+   +   +
9   4   5
= 18 = 18 = 18

A Use a calculator. Find the **magic number**
and the **missing numbers** in each magic square.

1.
4	3	8
9		
		6

Magic number

2.
15		13
	16	
		17

Magic number

3.
47		49
52		
51		53

Magic number

4.
16	3	2	13
		11	
9	6	7	12
4			1

Magic number

5.
23			26
		21	
22	16	17	
11	25		14

Magic number

6.
19	61		96
98		69	11
66	18		
81		16	

Magic number

Name _____

Class _____

INVESTIGATING MAGIC SQUARES

© Unwin Hyman
Calculated to Please 2

Square magic 2

⮟

(35) ●●●●●●

B Set the calculator for **add 37** like this.
Use it to **add 37** to each number
to make a new magic square.

13	18	11
12	14	16
17	10	15

➡

Magic
number ☁   ⟶   Magic
number ☁

C Set the calculator for **subtract 27** like this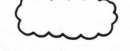
Use it to **subtract 27** from each number to make a new magic square.

71	66	67
64	68	72
69	70	65

➡

Magic
number ☁   ⟶   Magic
number ☁

D Set the calculator for **multiply by 7** like this
Use it to **multiply each number by 7** to make a new magic square.

14	9	10
7	11	15
12	13	8

➡

Magic
number ☁   ⟶   Magic
number ☁

Name _____   Class _____

INVESTIGATING MAGIC SQUARES.

© Unwin Hyman
Calculated to Please 2

Square magic 3

E Set the calculator for **divide by 8** like this. $8 \div \div = 0$
Use it to **divide each number by 8**
to make a new magic square.

88	144	104
128	112	96
120	80	136

➡

Magic number ⬭ → Magic number ⬭

F **Add** two magic squares to make a new magic square.

20	27	22
25	23	21
24	19	26

+

40	45	38
39	41	43
44	37	42

=

Magic number ⬭ → Magic number ⬭ → Magic number ⬭

G **Subtract** two magic squares to make a new magic square.

76	75	80
81	77	73
74	79	78

—

18	4	17
12	13	14
9	22	8

=

Magic number ⬭ → Magic number ⬭ → Magic number ⬭

. . . .

Name _____   Class _____

INVESTIGATING MAGIC SQUARES.

© Unwin Hyman
Calculated to Please 2

Equal shares and no spares 1, 2 and 3

● ● ● ● ● ●

Activity/Purpose

The activities involve the use of the constant function for division to examine a large number of examples, the patterns of which allow rules for divisibility to be suggested.

The rules of divisibility by 2, 10, 5, 3, 9 and 4 are considered in turn, and a brief statement of each rule is suggested and noted by the child.

Previous mathematical knowledge and skill required

Knowledge of tables of multiplication.
Experience of using the constant function.

Notes on using the pages

Use the pages in the order in which they appear.
Ensure that the constant function is understood to be an aid to the work which avoids repetitive key pressing.
Encourage the child to try numbers other than those given on the sheets. It is particularly important to test the rule on large numbers, for which the calculator is an ideal tool. Encourage the child to estimate or make a good guess at the likely display number. Careful use of estimation avoids the misreading of, for example, $17 \div 2 = 8\cdot5$ as $17 \div 2 = 85$.

● ● ● ● ● ●

Answers/Solutions

Numbers are exactly divisible by 2 if the units digit is $\left.\right\}$ *even.*
0, 2, 4, 6, 8.

Numbers are exactly divisible by 10 if the units digit is *zero.*

Numbers are exactly divisible by 5 if the units digit is *0* or *5.*

Numbers are exactly divisible by 3 if the *sum of the digits is divisible by 3.*

Numbers are exactly divisible by 9 if the *sum of the digits is divisible by 9.*

Numbers are exactly divisible by 4 if the *last two digits are exactly divisible by 4.*

EQUIPMENT

Calculator.

ADDITIONAL ACTIVITIES EXTENSIONS

1. Investigate the *largest numbers* which can be held in the display and which are divisible by 2, 10, 5, 3, 9 or 4.

2. Using the questions on divisibility by 3 and 9, investigate the effect of reversing each of the given numbers. Each will still be divisible by 3 or 9.

3. Encourage further examination and explanation of the section on divisibility by 4. Notice that the given numbers are 'paired'; the pairs having identical tens and units. Encourage the child to produce further pairs.

Equal shares and no spares 1

Set your calculator for **divide by 2** like this: [2] [÷] [÷] [=] [0]

Ring the bags of marbles that can be shared **exactly** among 2 people.

8 marbles

17 marbles

94 marbles

997 marbles

302 marbles

1011 marbles

756 marbles

Try some more numbers of your own.

10 000 marbles

533 marbles

189 marbles

106 marbles

Finish this sentence.

Numbers are exactly divisible by 2 if the units digit is _____ .

Set your calculator for **divide by 10** like this: [1] [0] [÷] [÷] [=] [0]

Ring the boxes of calculators that can be shared **exactly** among 10 schools.

30 calculators

144 calculators

110 calculators

1120 calculators

55 calculators

160 calculators

105 calculators

Try some more numbers of your own.

72 calculators

90 calculators

368 calculators

550 calculators

Finish this sentence.

Numbers are exactly divisible by 10 if the units digit is _____ .

Name _____ Class _____

RULES OF DIVISIBILITY BY 2 AND BY 10.

© Unwin Hyman
Calculated to Please 2

Equal shares and no spares 2 ㊳

Set your calculator for **divide by 5** like this: ⑤ ÷ ÷ = ⓪
Ring the packets of stamps that can be shared **exactly** among 5 people.

75 stamps all different

220 stamps all different

1000 stamps all different

125 stamps all different

96 stamps all different

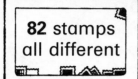
82 stamps all different

495 stamps all different

256 stamps all different

60 stamps all different

99 stamps all different

4865 stamps all different

Try some more numbers of your own.

Finish this sentence.

Numbers are exactly divisible by 5 if the units digit is

a _____ **or a** _____ .

Set your calculator for **divide by 3** like this: ③ ÷ ÷ = ⓪

Ring the piles of felt-tip pens that could be shared **exactly** among 3 people.

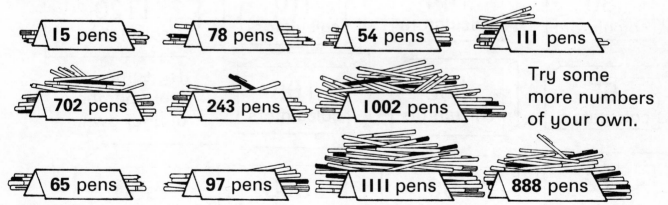

15 pens   78 pens   54 pens   111 pens

702 pens   243 pens   1002 pens

Try some more numbers of your own.

65 pens   97 pens   1111 pens   888 pens

Finish this sentence.

Numbers are exactly divisible by 3 if the sum of the digits is _____

_____ .

Name _____   Class _____

RULES OF DIVISIBILITY BY 5 AND BY 3.

© Unwin Hyman
Calculated to Please 2

Equal shares and no spares 3 ⓷⁹

Set your calculator for **divide by 9** like this: [9] [÷] [÷] [=] [0]

Ring the numbers which are **exactly** divisible by 9.

| 16 | 438 | 621 | 558 585 |

| 27 | 54 | 182 | 7585 |

| 9801 | 834 | Try some more numbers on the back of this sheet. |

Finish this sentence.
Numbers are exactly divisible by 9 if _____

_____ .

_____

Set your calculator for **divide by 4** like this: [4] [÷] [÷] [=] [0]

Ring the numbers which are **exactly** divisible by 4.

215 15 132

12 612 123 456 63 489 523

5096 96 256

45 1345 1020

120

2172 72 Try some more numbers of your own.

Finish this sentence.
Numbers are exactly divisible by 4 if

_____

_____

Name _____ Class _____

RULES OF DIVISIBILITY BY 9 AND BY 4.

© Unwin Hyman
Calculated to Please 2

Pattern spotting 1, 2 and 3

Activity/Purpose

The purpose of the activities is to encourage the child in recognising, recording, extending and describing patterns of numbers, using a calculator to generate the sequences.

The child:
- Completes the given key sequences and records the displays.
- Extends the pattern of numbers.
- Predicts the next line.
- Writes a sentence about the structure of the pattern.

Previous mathematical knowledge and skill required

Experience of using the four rules of number.
Understanding of place value.
Experience of the constant functions of the calculator.

Notes on using the pages

Use the pages in the order in which they appear.
An essential part of the activity is the prediction of the next stage in a sequence, and checking this prediction using the calculator.
Encourage the child to pencil in the prediction *before* checking.
To some extent the activity is self-checking, since there will be a pattern to be seen in both the input and output numbers.
Encourage the child to write a brief description of each pattern in the space provided. Allow various responses depending on ability, but encourage the child to be precise and 'say what he or she means'.
Encourage the use of the *constant function* of the calculator where appropriate, i.e. when repeating the same multiple.

Answers/Solutions

See opposite.

EQUIPMENT

Calculator.

ADDITIONAL ACTIVITIES EXTENSIONS

1. Encourage the child to continue and extend the sequence beyond the structure of the page. Most will overload the calculator after about six steps, but the pattern is likely to continue and could be checked using another calculating device (e.g. Napier's Rods).

2. An unnumbered blank of the sheet is provided at the back of the book for the child to create his or her own sequences up to 5 'steps' in length. Encourage *adaptation* of the given sequences, using small numbers, rather than a totally free choice.

N O T E S

Pattern spotting 1, 2 and 3

● ● ● ● ●

Answers/Solutions

Sheet 1

1.
$$1\times9+2=11$$
$$12\times9+3=111$$
$$123\times9+4=1111$$
$$1234\times9+5=11111$$
$$12345\times9+6=111111$$

2.
$$1\times9-1=8$$
$$21\times9-1=188$$
$$321\times9-1=2888$$
$$4321\times9-1=38888$$
$$54321\times9-1=488888$$

3.
$$1\times8+1=9$$
$$12\times8+2=98$$
$$123\times8+3=987$$
$$1234\times8+4=9876$$
$$12345\times8+5=98765$$

4.
$$9\times9+7=88$$
$$98\times9+6=888$$
$$987\times9+5=8888$$
$$9876\times9+4=88888$$
$$98765\times9+3=888888$$

5.
$$5\times9=45$$
$$55\times9=495$$
$$555\times9=4995$$
$$5555\times9=49995$$
$$55555\times9=499995$$

Sheet 2

1.
$$143\times7\times1=1001$$
$$143\times7\times2=2002$$
$$143\times7\times3=3003$$
$$143\times7\times4=4004$$
$$143\times7\times5=5005$$

2.
$$15873\times7\times1=111111$$
$$15873\times7\times2=222222$$
$$15873\times7\times3=333333$$
$$15873\times7\times4=444444$$
$$15873\times7\times5=555555$$

3.
$$12\times9=108$$
$$123\times9=1107$$
$$1234\times9=11106$$
$$12345\times9=111105$$
$$123456\times9=1111104$$

4.
$$9\times9=81$$
$$99\times9=891$$
$$999\times9=8991$$
$$9999\times9=89991$$
$$99999\times9=899991$$

5.
$$101\times11=1111$$
$$101\times111=11211$$
$$101\times1111=112211$$
$$101\times11111=1122211$$
$$101\times111111=11222211$$

Sheet 3

1.
$$33\times3367=111111$$
$$66\times3367=222222$$
$$99\times3367=333333$$
$$132\times3367=444444$$
$$165\times3367=555555$$

2.
$$6\times7=42$$
$$66\times67=4422$$
$$666\times667=444222$$
$$6666\times6667=44442222$$

3.
$$1\times99=99$$
$$12\times99=1188$$
$$123\times99=12177$$
$$1234\times99=122166$$
$$12345\times99=1222155$$

4.
$$9\times9=81$$
$$98\times9=882$$
$$987\times9=8883$$
$$9876\times9=88884$$
$$98765\times9=888885$$

5.
$$11\times11=121$$
$$111\times11=1221$$
$$1111\times11=12221$$
$$11111\times11=122221$$
$$111111\times11=1222221$$

Pattern spotting 1

Write the display for each calculation.
Guess the next line **before** you do it.
Write **two more** lines for each pattern.

Write a sentence about the pattern.

1.

$1 \times 9 + 2 =$

$12 \times 9 + 3 =$

$123 \times 9 + 4 =$

____ =

____ =

						1	1

2.

$1 \times 9 - 1 =$

$21 \times 9 - 1 =$

$321 \times 9 - 1 =$

____ =

____ =

							8

3.

$1 \times 8 + 1 =$

$12 \times 8 + 2 =$

$123 \times 8 + 3 =$

____ =

____ =

							9

4.

$9 \times 9 + 7 =$

$98 \times 9 + 6 =$

$987 \times 9 + 5 =$

____ =

____ =

					8	8

5.

$5 \times 9 =$

$55 \times 9 =$

$555 \times 9 =$

____ =

____ =

					4	5

Write the display for each calculation.
Guess the next line **before** you do it.
Write **two more** lines for each pattern.

Write a sentence
about the pattern.

1.
143 × 7 × 1 =

| | | | | | 1 | 0 | 0 | 1 |

143 × 7 × 2 =

143 × 7 × 3 =

〰〰〰 =

〰〰〰 =

2.
15 873 × 7 × 1 =

| | | 1 | 1 | 1 | 1 | 1 | 1 |

15 873 × 7 × 2 =

15 873 × 7 × 3 =

〰〰〰 =

〰〰〰 =

3.
12 × 9 =

| | | | | | 1 | 0 | 8 |

123 × 9 =

1234 × 9 =

〰〰〰 =

〰〰〰 =

4.
9 × 9 =

| | | | | | | 8 | 1 |

99 × 9 =

999 × 9 =

〰〰〰 =

〰〰〰 =

5.
101 × 11 =

| | | | | 1 | 1 | 1 | 1 |

101 × 111 =

101 × 1111 =

〰〰〰 =

〰〰〰 =

Name _____

Class _____

INVESTIGATING CALCULATOR PATTERNS OF NUMBERS.

© Unwin Hyman
Calculated to Please 2

Pattern spoting 3

Write the display for each calculation.
Guess the next line **before** you do it.
Write **two more** lines for each pattern.

Write a sentence
about the pattern.
↓

1.

33 × 3367 =
66 × 3367 =
99 × 3367 =

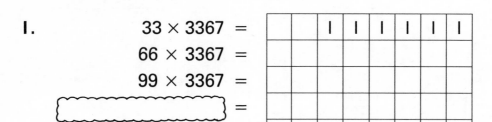

2.

6 × 7 =
66 × 67 =

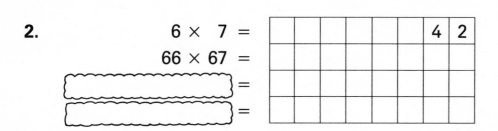

3.

1 × 99 =
12 × 99 =
123 × 99 =

4.

9 × 9 =
98 × 9 =
987 × 9 =

5.

11 × 11 =
111 × 11 =
1111 × 11 =

Name _____

Class _____

INVESTIGATING CALCULATOR PATTERNS OF NUMBERS.

© Unwin Hyman
Calculated to Please 2

Use only these keys ⟶ [C] [ ] [ ] [+] [−] [=]
on this sheet.

Fill in the keys you press to get the answer in the display.

1. ☐☐☐☐ [   ]
2. ☐☐☐☐ [   ]
3. ☐☐☐☐ [   ]
4. ☐☐☐☐ [   ]
5. ☐☐☐☐ [   ]
6. ☐☐☐☐ [   ]

Press [C] before each try!

Now do these. Make each target number.
Use as few keys as you can!
Write your answers in the boxes next to the targets.

7.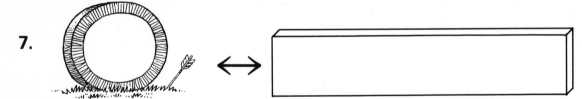

8.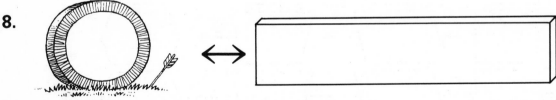

9.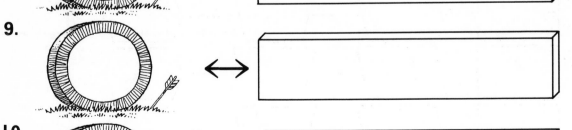

10.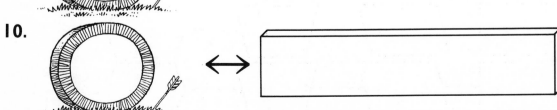

Name _____   Class _____

REVISION OF ADDITION AND SUBTRACTION SKILLS
CREATING A TRUE NUMBER SENTENCE, USING LIMITED KEYS.

© Unwin Hyman
Calculated to Please 2

Number Slimmer

Take ⬚ from each of these numbers.
Write down a **good guess** at the answer *before* you use a calculator!

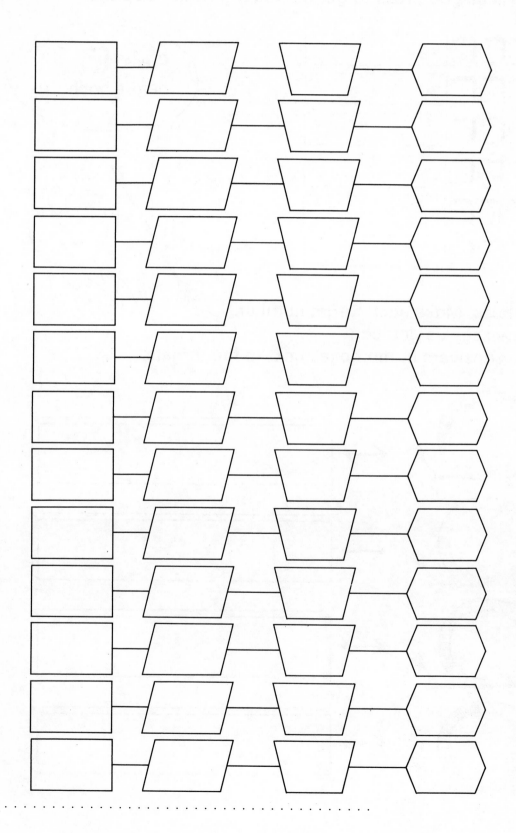

Name _____

Class _____

PLACE VALUE AND ESTIMATION PRACTICE (SUBTRACTING 1).

© Unwin Hyman
Calculated to Please 2

Times up !

● ● ● ● ● ● ●

Work out which of these numbers can be changed to [   ] by multiplying by a **whole** number.

Use your calculator!

Number	Yes or No	Show how here!
0		
1		
2		
3		
4		
5		
6		
7		
8		
9		
10		

If you have time, try some other numbers....

Name _____   Class _____

NUMBER INVESTIGATION. INTRODUCTION TO TESTS OF DIVISIBILITY.

© Unwin Hyman
Calculated to Please 2

Times up !

Work out which of these numbers can be changed to [   ] by multiplying by a **whole** number.

Use your calculator!

Number	Yes or No	Show how here!

If you have time, try some other numbers . . . .

Name _____ Class _____

NUMBER INVESTIGATION. INTRODUCTION TO TESTS OF DIVISIBILITY.

© Unwin Hyman
Calculated to Please 2

Four way split

4-way split

+	−	×	÷

Name _____

Class _____

USING THE FOUR RULES OF NUMBER TO REACH TARGET NUMBERS.

© Unwin Hyman
Calculated to Please 2

Hot hundreds 1

Use only numbers larger than 10.

Key in **one number** to change each starter to 100.

Key in **two different numbers** to change each starter to 100.

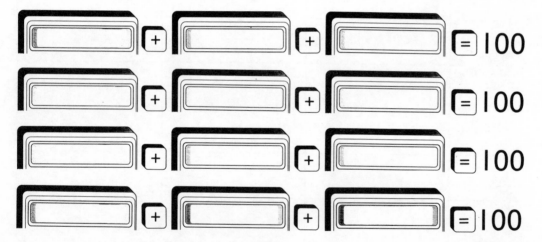

Key in **three different numbers** to change each starter to 100.

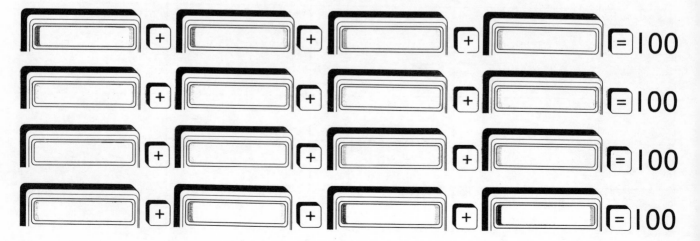

Name _____

Class _____

ESTIMATING AND CHECKING ADDITION OF NUMBERS TO 100.

© Unwin Hyman
Calculated to Please 2

Hot hundreds 2

Use only numbers larger than 10.

Start with 100. Key in **one number** to change it to the target.

Start with 100. Key in **two numbers** to change it to the target.

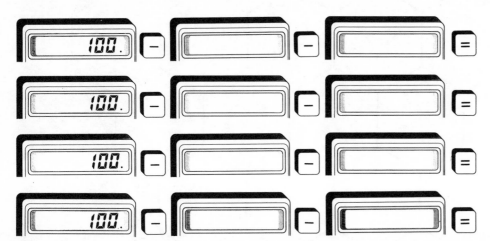

Start with 100. Key in **three numbers** to change it to the target.

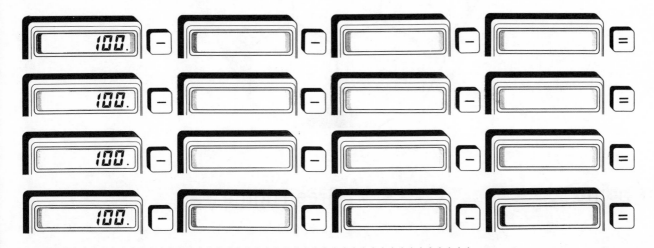

Name _____ Class _____

ESTIMATING AND CHECKING SUBTRACTION OF NUMBERS FROM 100.

© Unwin Hyman
Calculated to Please 2

CALC BUSTERS

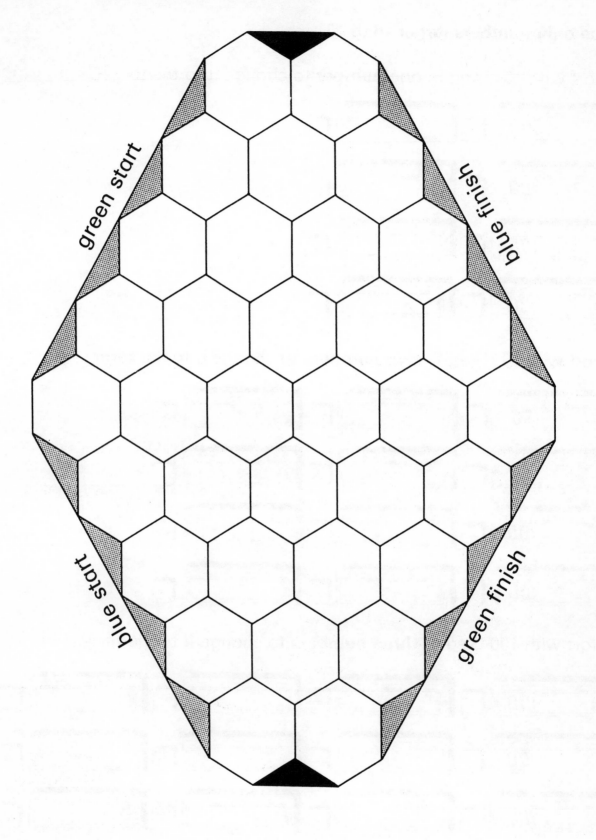

green start

blue finish

blue start

green finish

Blue name _____   **Green name** _____

Class _____

A GAME OF STRATEGY, USING MULTIPLICATION BONDS TO 132,
REINFORCED BY CALCULATOR USE.

© Unwin Hyman
Calculated to Please 2

Gobbler !

Gobbler is a sweet eater!
She always starts in the middle and
goes to an edge.
She can only move **up** ↑ or **down** ↓
or **right** → or **left** ←

The numbers show how many sweets
in each box.
Gobbler can only change direction ☐
after starting.
Colour Gobbler's journey to eat ☐ sweets.

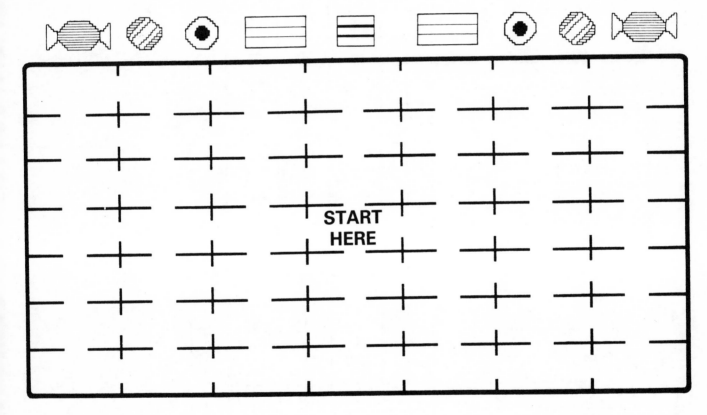

START HERE

At the end Gobbler was sick!

Name _____

ESTIMATION AND PROBLEM SOLVING.

© Unwin Hyman
Calculated to Please 2

Pattern spotting

Make up some patterns of your own.

Write them here	Show the displays here	Write a sentence about your pattern here
↓	↓	↓

1. _____
   _____
   _____
   _____
   _____

2. _____
   _____
   _____
   _____
   _____

3. _____
   _____
   _____
   _____
   _____

4. _____
   _____
   _____
   _____
   _____

5. _____
   _____
   _____
   _____
   _____